SIMPLE SHORT WAVE RECEIVER
CONSTRUCTION

Other Titles of Interest

SIMPLE SHORT WAVE RECEIVER CONSTRUCTION

by

R. A. PENFOLD

BERNARD BABANI (publishing) LTD
THE GRAMPIANS
SHEPHERDS BUSH ROAD
LONDON W6 7NF
ENGLAND

Please Note

Although every care has been taken with the production of this book to ensure that any projects, designs, modifications and/or programs etc. contained herewith, operate in a correct and safe manner and also that any components specified are normally available in Great Britain, the Publishers do not accept responsibility in any way for the failure, including fault in design, of any project, design, modification or program to work correctly or to cause damage to any other equipment that it may be connected to or used in conjunction with, or in respect of any other damage or injury that may be so caused, nor do the Publishers accept responsibility in any way for the failure to obtain specified components.

Notice is also given that if equipment that is still under warranty is modified in any way or used or connected with home-built equipment then that warranty may be void.

© 1990 BERNARD BABANI (publishing) LTD

First Published — August 1990

British Library Cataloguing in Publication Data
Penfold, R. A.
Simple shortwave receiver construction.
1. Shortwave radio equipment : Receivers, Construction — Amateurs' manual
I. Title
621.38418

ISBN 0 85934 220 4

Printed and bound in Great Britain by Cox & Wyman Ltd, Reading

Preface

Short wave radio has maintained a high level of popularity over many years. A steady stream of technical advances has resulted in the hobby changing in many respects, particularly in recent years with the massive advances in electronics that have occurred, but searching for transmissions from distant stations using simple receiving equipment is as fascinating now as it ever was. Picking up weak "DX" stations using simple home constructed equipment provides a sense of achievement and a degree of satisfaction that is perhaps lacking when similar stations are received using expensive commercial "black boxes".

This book provides some simple short wave receiver designs that can be constructed at only a fraction of the cost of new ready-made communications receivers, but which, nevertheless, enable interesting stations from all over the world to be received. Stripboard layouts and wiring diagrams are provided for all these designs, making them suitable projects for those with little or no previous experience of electronic project construction. Designs for both broadcast and amateur bands reception are included. Chapter 1 provides a substantial amount of background information on the short wave bands and short wave listening. No previous knowledge of short wave radio is assumed, and this book is suitable for complete beginners as well as those with some experience of radio and electronics.

R. A. Penfold

Contents

Chapter 1

SHORT WAVE BASICS

In recent years a number of new technology hobbies have emerged, but despite these distractions the well established hobby of short wave radio seems to have maintained a high degree of popularity. Over the years this hobby has admittedly had its ups and downs, but it has always maintained a fairly substantial following. Listening to, or even communicating with, stations hundreds or thousands of miles distant is, and probably always will be, a deeply fascinating experience. In order to operate an amateur bands transmitter it is necessary to obtain a radio amateurs licence, but one of these is only granted after one or two examination certificates have been obtained by the applicant. Initially at least, most people settle for short wave reception on the amateur and short wave broadcast bands. Some people go on to study for and (usually) gain an amateur radio licence, while others are content to remain short wave listeners. Either way it is one of the most interesting and absorbing hobbies you can take up.

The topic of short wave radio tends to conjure up images of large racks of equipment and vast arrays of aerials costing thousands of pounds. You can go straight out and buy a huge setup of this type if you have that sort of money to spend, but few people can afford to start this way. Even if you do have the resources to buy an expensive system right from the start, it probably does not make sense to do so. Short wave radio is a great hobby, but it might not be the right hobby for you! It is advisable to start with some modest equipment to see if the hobby appeals to you. It probably will, and you may quickly outgrow your initial equipment, but this introduction to the hobby will have cost little and should have taught you a great deal. This will stand you in good stead when moving on to more sophisticated equipment, which you should quickly learn to "drive". Jumping straight in with masses of complex equipment runs a real risk of getting overwhelmed by it all, getting frustrated at being unable to operate everything properly, and giving up.

There are three basic routes into the hobby of short wave radio. One is to find someone who pursues this hobby, or perhaps to join a local radio club, so that you can see a short wave radio system in operation, try it out, and generally get acquainted with things. This is possibly the best method, but may not be a practical proposition for everyone. Option number two is to buy an inexpensive short wave radio, add a short length of wire to act as an aerial, and then tune around the bands to see what you can pick up. This is quite a good way of entering the hobby, but has the disadvantage that you need to choose a receiver carefully, and as a beginner you will probably not know exactly what to look for when choosing a set. It would be very easy to spend a fair sum of money on a receiver that would be considerably less than ideal for your purposes. If you decide to take this route, I would strongly recommend reading as much as possible about the hobby in general, and short wave radios in particular, before deciding on which set to purchase.

The third route, and the one that I took many years ago, is to build your own receiver. A simple receiver need not cost very much to build, and while it may not offer particularly spectacular performance, it should enable you to receive countless interesting stations. It will probably teach you a great deal very quickly, and at very low cost. Obviously you need to be reasonably practical in order to build your own receiver, but you do not need to be an electronics expert to put together one or two simple sets.

This book provides a few simple do-it-yourself short wave receiver designs intended specifically for beginners. It also provides some useful background information that should help constructors to get the most from these receivers. You can simply set up a short wave installation and start tuning across each range to see what you can pick up, but this can easily lead to frustration at the lack of results. A lot of wasted time can be avoided if you know where and when it is likely to be worthwhile searching for stations.

Frequencies
The short wave range extends from about 1.7MHz to 30MHz. The short wave bands carry on where the high frequency end

of the medium wave broadcast band leaves off. It carries on a long way, and whereas the medium wave band is not much more than 1MHz wide, the short wave range covers over 28 MHz. This wide range of frequencies is subject to various international agreements which have split the range into numerous bands which have each been allocated some specific purpose. These include such things as marine, aeronautical, broadcast, and amateur bands. For the short wave listener it is really only the broadcast bands and the amateur bands that are of any interest. In fact listening in to other broadcasts may not be strictly legal. Anyway, in this book we will only be concerned with broadcast and amateur band listening.

The broadcast bands contain some transmissions that are not unlike our domestic radio stations, and those from other countries that can be picked up on the medium waveband. However, much of the output on these bands is not intended for home consumption in the country from which the transmissions emanate. A substantial percentage of the output is aimed at foreign lands, and is either designed to enlighten people in other countries about the country producing the programmes, or it is just straightforward propaganda. I suppose that it is fair to say that in a fair proportion of cases it actually falls somewhere between these two extremes. Anyway, a short wave transmission from (say) Sweden might be in Swedish, but it would be just as likely to be in English and aimed at an English audience, or Russian and aimed at a Russian audience.

Many short wave stations around the world produce programmes that are in the English language, either for the consumption of audiences in the British Isles, or for people in other English speaking countries around the world. The English language programmes aimed at Britain are the easiest proposition for the short wave listener, and represent a good starting point. They are transmitted on frequencies and at times that give a good chance of them being received at good strength in Britain, and with the station identifications given in English it is easy to find out what stations you are receiving. Most broadcast stations use directional aerials that concentrate the signal in the direction of the target country, and this also helps to ensure that these transmissions are received at

3

good strength in Britain.

English transmissions aimed at other countries represent a more difficult "target". The aerials will in most cases be well and truly aimed in the wrong direction, and the transmission times/frequencies will not be chosen to give good reception in Britain.

Some short wave transmissions are intended for home consumption, and the main example of these are the ones that are found on the low frequency broadcast bands, or "tropical" bands as they are often called. Apparently, in some tropical regions, particularly in South America, lightning causes severe interference on the medium waveband and so these short wave bands are used for domestic radio services, as they are less affected by this problem. These two categories of transmission represent an interesting challenge for the experienced short wave listener (s.w.l.), but would provide a rather difficult starting point.

The amateur bands are used by private individuals to communicate with each other across the world, or maybe just across town. The maximum permitted powers on the amateur bands fall well short of the high levels used by many broadcast stations. The aerials used are generally more modest as well. On some bands short distance communications is often all that is possible, but on all the amateur bands, if the prevailing conditions are favourable, world wide communications is possible. Due to the relatively low transmitter powers used, and the forms of modulation used by most amateurs, reception on these bands is in certain respects more demanding than reception of the broadcast bands. Some very simple short wave receiver designs for the home constructor are not well suited to amateur bands reception, including some of the designs featured in this book. However, one of the designs is specifically aimed at amateur band reception, and will give quite good results.

Finding the country of origin of amateur band stations is not usually too difficult. These stations have call signs which they must give at frequent intervals, and the first one or two letters of the callsign indicate the country in which the station is operating ("G" in the case of U.K. amateur stations for example). Apart from the callsign, most amateur stations give their location ("QTH" in amateur radio jargon) with a fair degree of precision, together with basic details of the equipment they are using. English is used a good deal by radio amateurs from non-English speaking countries, and there is nothing unusual about two amateurs communicating in English when it is the native tongue of neither.

It is probably a good idea to try out both types of short wave listening at first. You can then specialise in whichever one you find the most interesting, or pursue both aspects of the hobby if you like. A term you are likely to encounter in both types of short wave listening is "DXing". This simply means trying to receive distant or otherwise difficult to pick up radio stations. If you become a competent short wave listener, you are then a "DXer".

There are now thirteen short wave broadcast bands. These are listed below, together with the frequency span of each one.

Table 1 (Short Wave Broadcast Bands)

Band	Frequency Range
120 Metres	2.3MHz to 2.498MHz
90 Metres	3.2MHz to 3.4MHz
75 Metres	3.95MHz to 4.0MHz
60 Metres	4.75MHz to 5.06MHz
49 Metres	5.95MHz to 6.2MHz
41 Metres	7.1MHz to 7.3MHz
31 Metres	9.5MHz to 9.9MHz
25 Metres	11.65MHz to 12.05MHz
22 Metres	13.6MHz to 13.8MHz
19 Metres	15.1MHz to 15.6MHz
16 Metres	17.55MHz to 17.9MHz
13 Metres	21.45MHz to 21.85MHz
11 Metres	25.6MHz to 26.1 MHz

It is only fair to point out that it is not unknown for the short wave broadcast bands to spill over the band limits somewhat. As a quick demonstration of this point I tried tuning a sensitive short wave set at frequencies beyond the 7.3MHz upper limit of the 41 metre band. There were plenty of broadcast stations to be found betwen 7.3MHz and 7.4MHz, and there were even a few stations beyond 7.4MHz. It therefore pays to scan more than the official frequency range of most short wave broadcast bands.

The amateur bands frequency allocations are much more rigidly enforced, and any station straying outside the official band limits by even a very small amount could well be required to close down (perhaps permanently). There are currently nine short wave amateur bands, and these plus their frequency spans are listed below. Incidentally, the 160 metre band is popularly known as "topband", but the other bands seem to lack any nickname of this type.

Table 2 (Short Wave Amateur Bands)

Band	Frequency Range
160 Metres	1.8MHz to 1.85MHz (2.0MHz)
80 Metres	3.5MHz to 3.8MHz (4.0MHz)
40 Metres	7.0 MHz to 7.1MHz (7.3MHz)
29.5 (30) Metres	10.1MHz to 10.15MHz
20 Metres	14.0MHz to 14.35MHz
16.5 (17) Metres	18.068MHz to 18.168MHz
15 Metres	21.0MHz to 21.45MHz
12 Metres	24.89MHz to 24.99MHz
10 Metres	28MHz to 29.7MHz

In some countries, including the U.K., 160 metres has an upper limit of 2.0MHz, whereas in other countries it ends at 1.85MHz. Similarly, in some countries the 80 metre band extends right up to 4.0MHz, and the 40 metre band extends to 7.3MHz. Note that in the U.K. these bands end at the 3.8MHz and 7.1MHz limits. Some of these bands are not exclusively for amateur use, and other stations (such as maritime types) will be found within these bands. It is mainly the low frequency bands where these other transmissions are to be found.

Propagation

It is important to realise that the various bands have different characteristics. Some bands are best suited to short or medium distance communications, while others good for long distant reception and are virtually useless for short distance work. Factors such as the time of day, time of the year, and position in the sunspot cycle also have a profound effect on band conditions. For example, some bands provide long distance reception with ease during daylight hours, but usually fade out altogether soon after darkness falls. In fact the higher frequency bands are "dead" and unusable for much of the time!

If we start with the lower frequency bands, these are the ones at frequencies of about 10MHz or lower. Local reception via the ground wave is good at virtually any time of the day or year on these bands. The ground wave is simply direct communication from point A to point B, as in Figure 1.1. The distance that can be covered depends very much on the output power used, the efficiency of the aerial, etc. On

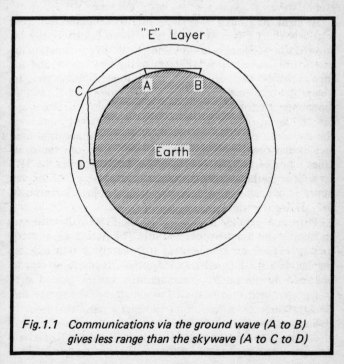

Fig.1.1 Communications via the ground wave (A to B) gives less range than the skywave (A to C to D)

the 160 metre amateur band only low transmitter powers are used, and the range provided by the ground wave is typically only about 30 miles or less. With ground wave communications the range obtained is always to a significant extent dependent on the terrain. The ground wave is not strictly a line-of-sight means of communications, but it does not have any great abilities to overcome the curvature of the earth, hills, mountains, or any large obstructions. The low powers used on 160 metres make it especially vulnerable to "blind" spots caused by the local terrain.

On the other amateur bands somewhat higher powers are possible, and a range of as much as a few hundred miles can be obtained using the ground wave. Similarly, with the high powers used on the low frequency broadcast bands it is possible to obtain a range of several hundred miles using the ground wave.

At night the ground wave still provides communication over relatively short distances, but greater distances can usually be covered due to changes in the atmosphere. In particular, radio waves can penetrate the "D" layer of the atmosphere, and are then reflected back to earth by the ionised "E" layer. In Figure 1.1 the line that goes through points A, C, and D represents the route taken by the radio waves reflected from the "E" layer. Obviously the route to some extent overcomes the curvature of the earth, and permits communication over greater distances to be achieved. In fact ranges of a thousand miles or more are possible. Although reflection via the "E" layer is something that does not generally occur during the hours of daylight, this does sometimes happen, but usually only during the winter months.

Propagation on the high frequency bands is totally different to that on the low frequency bands. The ground wave is very ineffective at high frequencies, and the signal that radiates parallel or almost parallel to the ground tends to be rapidly absorbed by the earth. Communication via the ground wave at high frequencies is restricted to something close to true line of sight communication. This provides a range that is likely to be just a few miles at best.

Although this might seem like a disadvantage, it does have a strong positive aspect. On the low frequency bands at night it is possible to obtain a range of a thousand miles or more, but there is often strong interference from relatively local stations to contend with when trying to receive distant stations. The lack of ground wave on the high frequency bands virtually eliminates problems with interference from local stations. There is a negative aspect to the absorption of the ground wave though. At times when the atmosphere does not reflect the radio signals back to earth, neither long distance nor local communications is possible. The high frequency bands therefore fade out at times and are totally free of any receivable transmissions. It is extremely unusual for the low frequency bands to go "dead" in this way, but it is a state that exists for a fair percentage of the time on the high frequency bands.

There is a difference in the way that the atmosphere reflects high and low frequency transmissions. As already explained, low frequency signals are reflected from the ionised "E" layer, which is a comparatively low layer of the atmosphere. High frequency signals always pass through this layer, and it is a higher layer (the "F2" layer) that sometimes becomes ionised and reflects these signals. Having the signal reflected from a higher layer is advantageous for long distance communications, since it obviously enables the signals to reach further around the world (route A − B − C in Figure 1.2). The radio waves at shallow angles to the earth will be reflected, and due to their shallow angle will cover a vast distance before they return to earth. Although it might seem that short range communications would be provided by high angle reflected radio waves, this is not the case. High angle signals always pass straight through the atmosphere (route A − D in Figure 1.2).

Communications over really long distances, whether on the low or high frequency bands, requires the radio signal to be repeatedly bounced from the atmosphere to the earth, back up to the atmosphere, down to earth again, and so on, as in Figure 1.3. There are obviously tremendous losses, and very little of the signal gets through to the receiver. However, communications from one side of the earth to the other is perfectly possible, and quite frequently achieved. In fact signals from the other side of the world can be surprisingly strong on the highest of the high frequency bands. One

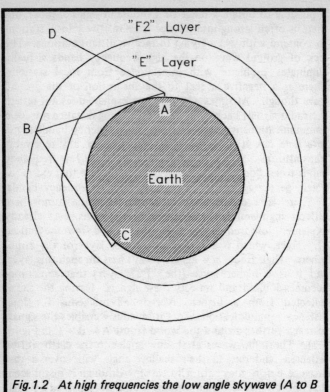

Fig.1.2 At high frequencies the low angle skywave (A to B to C) provides communications over long distances

theory has the signals being channelled by the upper atmosphere when these very strong signals get through, since the multiple bounce route would not seem to provide a good enough route for such strong signals. Which of the two routes they take is largely academic, and the important thing is that under the right atmospheric conditions, worldwide communication is possible on the short wave bands.

The ionisation of the "F2" layer occurs during the hours of daylight, and consequently it is during daylight hours that the high frequency bands are most active. These bands often

10

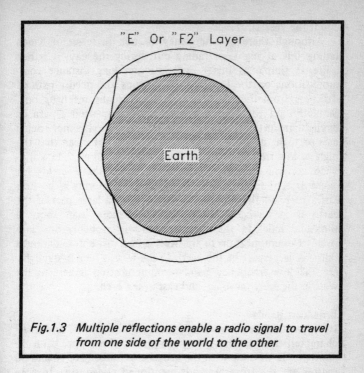

"E" Or "F2" Layer

Earth

Fig.1.3 Multiple reflections enable a radio signal to travel from one side of the world to the other

fade out totally at night. They tend to be at their best during the summer months when the days are long, and at their worst during the winter months when the days are short.

Sunspot activity is also an important factor controlling propagation conditions on the high frequency bands. Sunspots go through peaks and troughs of activity on an approximately eleven year cycle. For low frequency band reception it is generally the troughs of sunspot activity that provide the best long distance communications, but these bands are less affected by highs and lows of sunspot activity. On the high frequency bands it is the peaks of activity that bring the best conditions for long distance reception. I am writing this in 1990, which is more or less the peak of the current cycle. The number of sunspots should steadily reduce over the next five or six years, then increase again to reach a new peak round about the year 2001.

Although there is a tendency to talk in terms of bands fading out at night, or fading out during the day, it is not quite as simple as this. For optimum long distance communications on the low frequency bands you need a path of darkness from the transmitting station to the receiving one. Similarly, on the high frequency bands you need a path of daylight from the transmitter to the receiver. It simply being day or night at the receiving station does not mean that the high or low frequency bands (respectively) will provide world-wide communications. On the high frequency bands for example, communications to the east will normally be best fairly early in the morning. At this time a large part of the earth is in daylight to the east, but more than about a thousand miles to the west the sun will probably not have risen. Communication to the west is best just before darkness falls. A large part of the earth to the west is then in daylight. On the low frequency bands communication is best to the west in the early morning, and east in the evening.

Broadcast Bands

It is worthwhile considering each of the bands, and their characteristics, as these vary so much from one band to another. If we start with the broadcast bands, 120, 90 and 60 metres are the tropical bands mentioned previously. In non-tropical regions they are also used for other purposes, and this means that DXers using these bands often have a lot of interference from non-broadcast stations to contend with. DX stations can be received in the U.K. using these bands, but it requires a fair amount of skill and is certainly a lot easier using good quality equipment. This high difficulty factor tends to attract the more experienced DXers.

The 75 metre band is an international broadcast band, but this band is another one that is shared with other services. This band provides long distance reception after dark, but it does not seem to be particularly popular with either broadcasters or listeners.

The 49, 41, and 31 metre bands are the main broadcast bands, and are usually crammed with stations at any time of the day or night. They are low frequency bands, and as such they are good for short to medium distance reception during the hours of daylight, and longer distance reception during the hours of darkness. As the ground wave is not absorbed by the earth, interference from relatively close stations is something that often has to be contended with when seeking out weak DX stations. These bands are so crowded with powerful transmissions that interference from other stations is a frequent problem even during short to medium distance reception.

25 metres is generally considered to be a high frequency band, and accordingly it does normally provide good reception during daylight hours. It will not always fade out after dark though, and it will often provide good reception throughout the night. This is a band which has excellent DX potential, and which seems to be much used by the broadcasters these days. The 22 metre band is a new one which has similar characteristics to the 25 metre band. However, being relatively new and one of the smaller bands it does not carry as many stations as the 25 metre band.

The 19, 16, and 13 metre bands are true high frequency types that will normally provide excellent reception over large distances provided there is a path of daylight between the transmitting and receiving stations. Absorption of the ground wave by the earth eliminates problems with interference from nearby stations. Like all true high frequency bands these are better in the summer months than during the winter months with their short hours of daylight.

The 11 metre band is another true high frequency type, but being close to the upper limit of the short wave spectrum it is more affected by the prevailing conditions than are the other bands. In addition to being at its best during the summer months, it is also given a substantial boost when sunspot activity is high. Presumably due to its rather unpredictable nature, the broadcasters seem to be a bit reluctant to use this band. When conditions are right though, it offers the ultimate in broadcast DXing. When conditions are bad it goes "dead" for long periods of time, and there are probably few stations transmitting at these times anyway. It is certainly an interesting band to use when it is showing signs of life.

Amateur Bands

The 160 metre band ("topband") is a difficult DXing band for two main reasons. One is that the maximum power for this band in the U.K. is just 10 watts, which compares to 150 watts on the other short wave amateur bands (or as much as 1000 watts in some countries). There are similar restrictions on the maximum output power for this band in many countries. The second reason is that this band is shared with maritime radio services, and these generate strong signals that can cause severe interference when trying to receive weak DX stations. As a DX band it is probably one for the more experienced operators. At one time it was the established band for local contacts, but it seems to have been usurped from this role by the v.h.f. and u.h.f. amateur bands. These offer a large number of channels and relative freedom from interference from other stations.

The 80 metre band provides a range of up to a few hundred miles during daylight hours, and a few thousand miles during the hours of darkness. In fact there is the potential for the reception of stations anywhere in the world during the hours of darkness. This band is shared with other radio services, and contending with interference from these is a major problem. Note that the U.K. frequency allocation for 80 metres has a high frequency limit of 3.8MHz, but in some countries (notably the U.S.A.) the upper limit is at 4.0MHz. American stations can often be heard in the 3.8MHz to 4.0MHz segment of the band during the small hours of the night.

40 metres seems to have gained considerably in popularity over recent years. At one time it was little used, particularly after dark. One drawback is that it is a small band just 100 kHz wide, giving a very limited number of channels. In some countries (including the U.S.A.) it extends up to 7.3MHz, which compares to 7.1MHz in the U.K. and many other countries. The main problem though, is that it is right next to the 41 metre broadcast band. In days gone by a number of broadcast stations used to transmit within the 40 metre band frequency allocation. The 7.1MHz to 7.3MHz portion of the band actually overlaps the 41 metre broadcast band, and receiving amateur stations in this part of the band can be very difficult indeed. This all makes conditions very difficult on

this band, particularly after dark. Remember that broadcast bands use much higher powers than amateur stations, and generally have much more sophisticated aerial systems as well. Conditions have improved somewhat in recent years, with broadcast stations tending not to spill over at this end of the band anything like as much as in the past. The close proximity of the 41 metre band with its plethora of powerful transmissions still remains a problem, but 40 metres has good DX potential. It is normally possible to receive many European stations during daylight hours, and worldwide reception is possible during the hours of darkness.

The 20 metre band is the one generally regarded as most suitable for long distant reception. It mostly fades out as darkness falls, or soon afterwards, but it provides excellent DX reception during daylight hours. Worldwide reception is often possible, and probably the only drawback of this band is that its popularity often leads to overcrowding and adjacent channel interference when trying to receive weak DX stations.

In most respects the 15 metre band is very similar to the 20 metre band. Covering a high range of frequencies means that it is a bit less reliable and more unpredictable. It has good DX potential during daylight hours though. The 10 metre band is at high frequencies, almost right to the upper limit of the short wave spectrum in fact. This makes it very dependent on sunspot activity, and when the sunspot cycle is near its minimum the 10 metre band will usually fade out totally for long periods of time. When the sunspot cycle is near its peak the situation is reversed. The band remains open for much of the time, and stations on the other side of the world are sometimes received at strengths that would suggest they were on the other side of the road! When conditions are right it offers the greatest DX potential, but when conditions are bad it is devoid of any signals for most of the time.

It is worth noting that there is a convention that the low frequency end of each amateur band is used for c.w. (continuous wave, or morse in other words), while the remainder of each band is used for phone (voice) and c.w. communications. This would seem to be a convention rather than a strictly enforced rule, and phone stations are generally to be found encroaching into the low frequency halves of these bands. This is perhaps not surprising as phone communication seems to be more popular than morse code these days. However, phone stations are generally a bit "thin on the ground" in the low frequency sections of the bands.

Aerials

Aerials for short wave receivers can be quite complex, and require vast amounts of space. For the receivers featured in this book a simple wire antenna will suffice, and will give quite good results. For any short wave system it is not just a matter of getting strong enough signals, it is also a matter of sorting out the required weak DX signal from masses of much stronger signals. The difference in the strengths of the most powerful signals on the band and weak DX ones is often enormous. The strongest signals could be at levels of a few hundred millivolts, with weak DX signals at perhaps just a few microvolts, one hundred thousandth as strong. Even sophisticated communications receivers sometimes have problems sorting out weak signals from amongst much stronger ones, and it is certainly a problem with simple receivers such as the ones featured in this book. These sets will work with more complex aerials, but there is a real danger that the stronger signals from such aerials would simply overload the sets for much of the time. It is probably best to settle for simple aerials until you progress to more sophisticated receivers, but there is obviously no harm in experimenting with various types of aerial if this is an aspect of the hobby that you find particularly interesting.

A simple wire antenna is just a length of wire that is connected to the aerial socket of the receiver at one end, and nothing at the other end. At its most simple it just consists of a telescopic aerial, or just a few feet of wire attached to a shelf, picture rail, or whatever. An aerial as short as this will not usually provide very good results, although a number of stations may be received. A somewhat longer aerial is definitely preferable, as is one mounted out of doors. If circumstances do not permit the use of an outdoor aerial, then use some aerial wire mounted indoors, around a picture rail, in the loft, or wherever you can accommodate it. In general, the aerial will work best if it is as long as possible, and

16

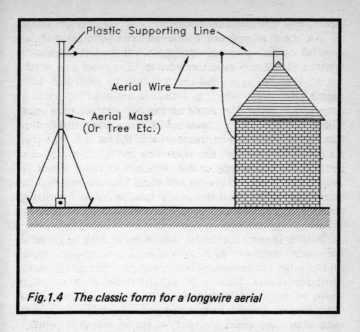

Fig.1.4 The classic form for a longwire aerial

mounted as high as possible. A fairly straight piece of wire is probably best, but it can be taken around (say) two or three sides of a room if that is the best that can be done. Wire specifically intended for use in aerial applications can be obtained, but ordinary multi-strand p.v.c. insulated connecting wire, or about 16 to 22 s.w.g. enamelled copper wire will both work well.

The classic outdoor aerial uses an arrangement along the lines of Figure 1.4. It is probably not worthwhile going to the substantial expense of a proper aerial mast when first trying your hand at short wave radio, but something like a shed, high fence, or tree might happen to be in a suitable position to make a good fixing point for the far end of the aerial. For optimum results the aerial should be, in the main, well clear of buildings or other large obstructions.

The aerial wire needs to be well insulated from the earth, or anything that is in electrical contact with the earth. In practice this means the house, the support for the far end of the aerial, and practically anything that the aerial might touch. If the aerial should come into electrical contact with an earthed object, some of the signal will be lost straight to earth, and will not reach the receiver. The aerial wire should be an insulated type, and this will help to avoid significant signal losses. However, it is normal to use more insulation at any points where the aerial comes into contact with something, which usually means where it enters and is attached to the house, and where it is supported at the far end. As shown in Figure 1.4, some plastic supporting line is normally used to provide insulation between the aerial and its fixing points. It might also be a good idea to add some p.v.c. sleeving over the aerial wire at the point where it enters the house, in order to make sure that the wire is well and truly insulated from the house.

Within reason, the aerial should be as long as possible. About 20 metres or so of wire should give excellent results, even on the low frequency bands where a long aerial is usually a decided asset. There is probably nothing to be gained by using an aerial longer than about 40 metres. Even an aerial only about 10 metres long should provide good results in most situations. An aerial of this type (or an indoor antenna) is considerably less than ideal for reception on the low frequency bands, but should still provide reasonable results.

Earth Connection
An earth connection can improve reception, but is not likely to be worthwhile troubling about if you are only interested in reception on the high frequency bands. The increase in signal strength provided by an earth connection when using these bands is usually not noticeable. The situation is different for operation on the low frequency bands, and a good earth connection can result in a substantial boost in signal strengths, especially at frequencies of about 5MHz or lower. If you are interested in using the low frequency bands in earnest, either an earth connection or a fairly long aerial should be used, and ideally you should use both.

An earth connection simply consists of a piece of metal connected to a length of wire, with the metal buried in the ground. The free end of the wire connects to the earth socket

18

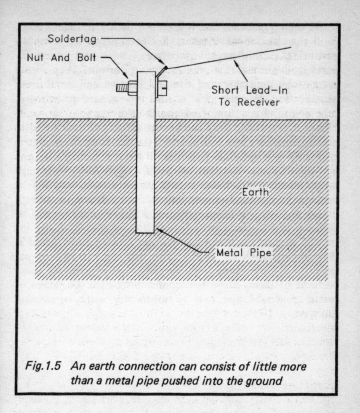

Fig.1.5 *An earth connection can consist of little more than a metal pipe pushed into the ground*

of the receiver. This wire should be of a fairly heavy gauge, and should be no longer than is absolutely necessary. The wire does not need to be an insulated type, since it will obviously not matter if it comes into contact with any earthed objects. However, it is probably best to use an insulated type so that the wire is protected against the elements. The piece of metal can be virtually any piece of scrap metal that is to hand. It must make good contact with the ground, and accordingly it should not be coated with paint or any other insulating substance. If necessary, clean off the surface of the metal with a wire brush, wire-wool, a solvent, or whatever is appropriate for removing the surface coating.

As already pointed out, it does not matter too much what form the piece of metal takes. For good efficiency it should have a reasonably large surface area, and would ideally be made from a metal that will not rapidly corrode. People have successfully used sheets of steel, biscuit tins, and metal pipes or rods. Probably the most popular type of earth is the metal tube or rod variety, and this generally takes the form shown in Figure 1.5. Provided the rod or tube is fairly narrow it can be easily hammered into most earth. On the other hand, if it is very narrow it will only have a small surface area and may not be very efficient. A tube about half a metre long and around 25 millimetres in diameter should act as a reasonably efficient earth electrode and should not be too difficult to install.

Do not use the mains earth, or a gas or water pipe as an earthing point. Using the mains earth is potentially dangerous in this context, as is using a gas pipe. Using a water pipe is potentially dangerous in that you might just mistake a gas pipe for a water type, and as many water pipes (or some sections of them) are made from non-metallic substances, it would probably not give a satisfactory earth connection anyway.

Chapter 2

CRYSTAL SET

A crystal set has several big advantages over other types of receiver. Firstly, it does not require a battery or any other power source. Obviously power is needed from somewhere in order to get the set to do something, but the only power involved is that which the aerial plucks out of the air. In other words, the power that drives the earphone is provided by the transmitter. A second advantage is that a crystal set is extremely simple, and it is therefore very easy to build. Thirdly, and as a result of its extreme simplicity, a crystal set is very inexpensive. Also, it is very easy to use, and requires no alignment or setting up procedures.

This might make it seem like an ideal receiver, but it has drawbacks that are at least as big as its advantages. The main one is simply that a crystal set has an abysmal level of performance. It is very insensitive, and requires a reasonable aerial in order to receive anything at all. A ferrite rod or short telescopic aerial are not good enough, and unless you happen to live very close to a transmitter, will provide reception of no stations whatever. A crystal set has very poor selectivity. In other words, if there are two stations very close together, the tuning control of the set might not let you pick out just one or the other. You may have to receive both at once, with the tuning control probably enabling the desired station to be received a bit more strongly than the one that is not required. The station in the background will be at a significant level, making reception of the wanted station quite difficult. In fact, if the interfering station is much stronger than the wanted one, it might not be possible to adjust the set so that the interfering signal is received at a lower level than the wanted one. It is then up to your hearing mechanism to try to sort things out!

A further drawback of crystal sets is that they can only resolve ordinary a.m. transmissions. As this is the type of transmission currently used by short wave broadcast stations this is not a major drawback. However, as ordinary a.m. is little used on the amateur bands, and the performance of a crystal set is inadequate for these bands anyway, a short wave crystal set has to be considered as strictly a broadcast bands receiver.

One final problem is that a crystal set does not provide sufficient output to drive a loudspeaker, and will often not give very good volume from even the most sensitive of headphones or earphones. The lack of loudspeaker output is not too important in a short wave listening context, since it is better to use headphones for this type of reception anyway. I do not really understand why, but copying weak signals through a lot of background noise seems to be noticeably easier using headphones rather than loudspeaker output.

I suppose the limitations of a crystal receiver preclude its use for "serious" short wave listening, but it is certainly something that is interesting to try, and a lot of fun can be had at very low cost. Receiving interesting stations is possible, but it requires a lot of patience and dedication. This is good training for DXing with a more sophisticated receiver, which will require no less patience and skill. If you decide to progress to building a more sophisticated receiver after a short while (as you probably will), remember that most of the components in the crystal set can be reused in a new receiver.

Amplitude Modulation

A radio signal is basically just an ordinary a.c. type, much the same as the U.K. a.c. mains supply, or the output signals from a hi-fi amplifier that drive the loudspeakers. The frequency of radio waves is much higher though. An a.c. signal has a voltage that first rises to a peak positive level, then falls back to zero, rises to a negative peak, and then falls back to zero again. This is one cycle, but a normal a.c. signal consists of numerous cycles following one after the other. A graph of time versus voltage gives the waveform of the signal, as in Figure 2.1. This waveform is a sinewave type incidentally.

The frequency of an a.c. signal is simply the number of cycles that occur during a one second period. For the U.K. mains supply for instance, there are 50 cycles per second. These days frequency is normally expressed in hertz (often abbreviated to "Hz") rather than cycles per second, and the

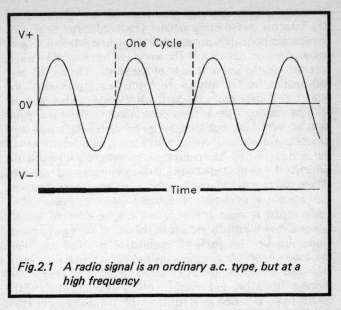

Fig.2.1 A radio signal is an ordinary a.c. type, but at a high frequency

mains supply is therefore at a frequency of 50Hz. High frequencies are usually expressed in either kilohertz (1 kilohertz [1kHz] = 1000Hz) or megahertz (1 megahertz [1MHz] = 1000000Hz or 1000kHz). The upper limit of the audio range is at about 20kHz, and this is more or less where the radio frequency spectrum begins. Immediately above the audio range there is a very low frequency radio band used for special purposes, then the standard long wave broadcast band above that, then a marine band, then the medium wave band above that, and then the short wave band commencing at around 1.7MHz. The lowest short wave frequencies are therefore well above the audio range, being about one hundred times higher than the highest frequencies that most people can hear.

If a radio frequency signal is coupled to an aerial, it radiates an electro-magnetic signal that can be picked up by another aerial some distance away. The electrical signal produced in the receiving aerial is an exact replica of the original (if we ignore any interference that is picked up), but would normally be at a very much lower level. The voltage produced in the receiving aerial is often less than one millionth of the voltage fed into the transmitting aerial. This is adequate to provide communications though, and with the right conditions a signal transmitted on one side of the world can be received at usable strength on the opposite side of the earth. There is no easy explanation for just why an aerial radiates a signal through the ether, and it is probably best just to accept that it does.

Transmitting a signal from point A and receiving it at point B is all very well, but in order to be useful the signal must contain information. At its most basic level information can be modulated onto the radio signal by switching it on and off, which is the method used when sending morse coded messages. The signal is switched on when the morse key is depressed, and off when it is released. Modulating speech or music onto a radio signal is more involved, but can be achieved using a process that is broadly similar to the on/off keying of a morse code signal. This form of modulation is called amplitude modulation, or just a.m., and instead of just having the signal switched on or off, it can be varied to any level (amplitude) between these two extremes. In practice the amplitude of the radio signal is varied in sympathy with the audio input level. Figure 2.2 shows example radio and audio waveforms, and the amplitude modulated signal that results from these. The radio frequency signal is called the carrier wave, which I suppose is a pretty apt description of its basic function.

Some signal processing is needed at the receiver in order to recover the audio modulation signal from the radio frequency signal. This is just a simple two stage process, and the first part of the processing is to rectify the signal. In other words, either the negative or the positive half cycles are removed. It does not matter which, but in the waveform diagram of Figure 2.3 it is the negative half cycles that have been removed. The second stage is some lowpass filtering. This removes the radio frequency half cycles, and leaves a signal that is equal to their average amplitude. As will be apparent from Figure 2.3, this leaves a signal that is the same as the original audio modulation signal. Strictly speaking, the output from the demodulator differs from the original audio signal in that it is a varying d.c. signal and not a true a.c. type. However, this is of little practical importance, and simply adding a coupling capacitor

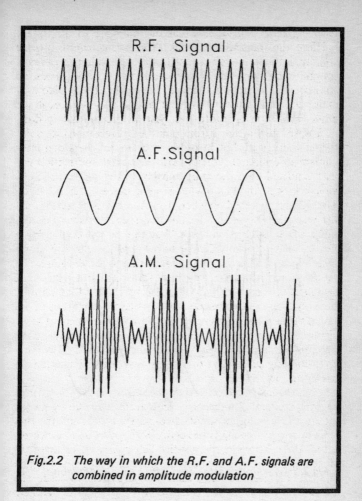

R.F. Signal

A.F. Signal

A.M. Signal

Fig.2.2 *The way in which the R.F. and A.F. signals are combined in amplitude modulation*

at the output would provide a true a.c. output signal anyway.

The Circuit
The circuit diagram for the crystal set appears in Figure 2.4, and this is of conventional design. The first function the set must provide is filtering that will pick out the desired radio

25

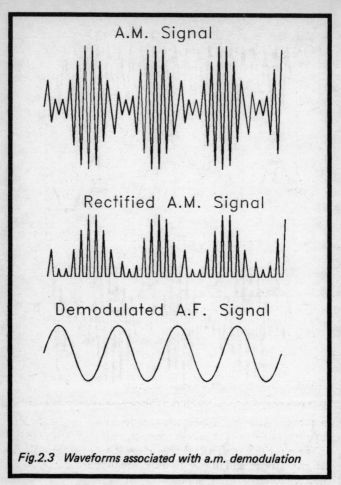

A.M. Signal

Rectified A.M. Signal

Demodulated A.F. Signal

Fig.2.3 Waveforms associated with a.m. demodulation

signal but which will, as far as possible, remove all the other signals. Remember that the aerial will pick up signals over a wide range of frequencies, from very low frequencies to beyond the upper limit of the short wave spectrum. The filtering of unwanted signals is provided by L1 and VC1. These form a parallel tuned circuit, and this type of circuit provides a very high impedance at or close to its resonant

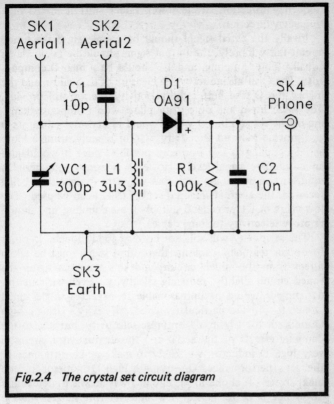

Fig.2.4   The crystal set circuit diagram

frequency. At other frequencies it provides an extremely low impedance. This gives the desired effect, with signals at or close to the resonant frequency being allowed to pass through to the next stage, and those at other frequencies being short circuited to earth and removed.

The resonant frequency of the tuned circuit can be adjusted by means of variable capacitor VC1, which therefore acts as a standard tuning control. With the specified values for VC1 and L1 the set has a coverage which extends from about 5.5 MHz to 15.5MHz. This provides coverage of several popular short wave broadcast bands. There is no harm in trying other values for L1. Higher values shift the coverage in the low

27

frequency direction, while lower values shift it in the high frequency direction.

Ideally the aerial signal should be coupled into the tuned circuit fairly loosely, the output signal should be taken via an equally loose coupling, and L1 should be a high Q component. The Q of an inductor is a measure of its quality, and the higher the Q, the better the selectivity the set will provide. The loose input and output couplings would minimise damping of the tuned circuit, which would effectively reduce its Q and provide reduced selectivity. Unfortunately, using a loose aerial coupling is not normally possible, since it would give an inadequate signal level. However, if a very long aerial is used, or conditions are such that very strong signals are being received, the alternative aerial socket (SK2) can be used. The low value of C1 provides a suitably loose coupling, and should improve selectivity to some degree.

The selectivity will still not be very good though. In order to obtain reasonable volume the output signal must be taken direct from the tuned circuit, and this tends to damp the tuned circuit slightly, reducing selectivity. Even without this damping it would be unreasonable to expect a single tuned circuit to provide particularly good selectivity. Using a high Q inductor for L1 should optimise selectivity, but due to the damping effects of the aerial and the demodulator circuit, a very high Q inductor is unlikely to make much difference to the set's performance. On trying a high Q inductor and an inexpensive r.f. choke in the circuit I was unable to detect any difference in performance. I would therefore suggest the use of an inexpensive choke for L1.

You might like to experiment with home-made coils. About ten turns of 24 s.w.g. enamelled copper wire on a tuning slug for a 10 millimetre (or thereabouts) coil former is a good starting point, or about double this number of turns on a non-ferrite core of about 6 to 10 millimetres in diameter (e.g. a piece of dowel) should suffice. Using more turns on the coil moves the coverage in the low frequency direction, or fewer turns moves it in the high frequency direction.

The demodulator circuit consists of D1, R1, and C2. Diode D1 rectifies the signal, and with the polarity shown in Figure 2.4 it allows positive half cycles to pass and blocks negative ones. However, if it is reversed, so that the negative half cycles are passed and the positive ones are blocked, the set will still work and provide exactly the same level of performance. Note that D1 is a germanium diode, and not a modern silicon type. Silicon diodes are not suitable for use in crystal receivers as they require a forward bias of about 0.5 volts or so before they will start to conduct properly. In most cases even the peak signal voltage from the tuned circuit would be inadequate to bring the diode into conduction, giving no output whatever. A germanium diode has a much lower forward conduction threshold voltage, and works well in this application.

The filtering is provided by capacitor C2. If the receiver is used with magnetic headphones R1 will not be necessary. It is important that there should be a discharge path for C2, as it will otherwise simply charge up to the peak voltage from D1, giving a steady d.c. output level with no audio signal superimposed on it. There is no need for a coupling capacitor at the output since earphones and headphones will work perfectly well from the varying d.c. signal provided by the demodulator.

It is important that the receiver should be used with a suitable type of earphone or headphones. Probably the best choice is a pair of high impedance (2k to 4k) magnetic headphones having good sensitivity. Headphones of this type now seem to be something of a rarity, and might prove to be impossible to obtain. Probably the next best choice is a crystal earphone. These offer good sensitivity, and are quite inexpensive. Medium impedance (about 600R) headphones might provide quite good results, but the sensitivity of these seems to vary enormously from one type to another. If you have a pair of medium impedance headphones it might be worth trying them with the set. Low impedance (about 8R) headphones and earphones are totally unsuitable for use with this receiver, as are the headphones of about 25 to 50 ohms impedance that are sold as replacements for use with personal stereo units.

Construction

With so few components there is not really much point in

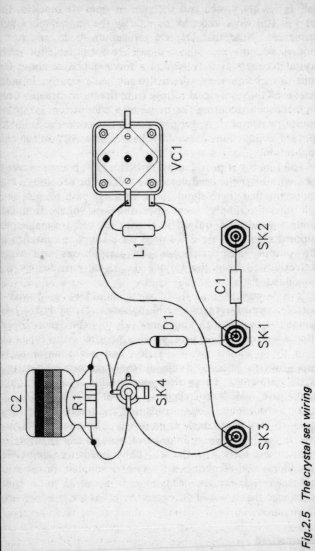

Fig.2.5 The crystal set wiring

using a circuit board of some kind for this project. A more practical method of construction is to simply hard-wire the small components onto VC1 and the sockets. Figure 2.5 provides details of the wiring.

Obviously the first step when constructing the unit is to mount the tuning control (VC1) and the four sockets on the front panel of the case. Virtually any small metal or plastic case should accommodate all the components with ease. The exact layout of the front panel is not too important from the electrical point of view, but try to use a layout that will enable the wiring to be kept quite short, and which will also be convenient when using the receiver. The headphone socket is a 3.5 millimetre jack type, and this will almost certainly require a 6.5 millimetre diameter mounting hole. A little confusingly, the normal (open construction) style 3.5 millimetre jack sockets have three tags and not two. This is due to the inclusion of switch contacts that can be used to automatically switch out a loudspeaker when an earphone is in use. This facility is clearly of no use in the current context, and one tag of the socket is consequently left unused. The two aerial and earth sockets are 4 millimetre types, or you may prefer to use the smaller 2 millimetre type. 4 millimetre sockets normally require 8 millimetre diameter mounting holes (5 millimetre diameter mounting holes are required for 2 millimetre sockets).

The mounting arrangements for variable capacitors tend to vary considerably from one type to another. Some require the usual 10 millimetre diameter mounting hole. Miniature types often require a hole of about 7 millimetres in diameter for their spindle, plus two smaller holes for miniature mounting bolts. For these the retailers' literature should give mounting details, or you may have to take some careful measurements from the variable capacitor itself. Note that some miniature variable capacitors are offered at very low prices, but have non-standard spindles that will not take standard push-on or grub-screw fixing control knobs. Some other type have spindles of the standard diameter, but of such short length it is difficult to find control knobs that can be fixed on them properly. Both types can be more trouble than they are worth, and are probably best avoided unless you are certain you can obtain a suitable control knob.

Last and by no means least, the popular Jackson "Type O" variable capacitors have an unusual mounting arrangement. They have a standard 6.35 millimetre diameter spindle which requires a hole in the panel of about 7 to 8 millimetres in diameter. They are fixed in position using three countersunk 4BA screws that fit into threaded holes in the front plate of the capacitor. The mounting screws are not normally supplied with the component, and must therefore be purchased separately. One way of marking the positions of these is to make a paper template with the aid of the variable capacitor itself. It is important that the mounting screws are short (no more than about 6 millimetres in length) or there is a real danger of them penetrating too far into the component and damaging its metal plates.

Although I have specified a value of 300p for VC1 in the components list, any value from about 250p to 500p should work perfectly well. A low value gives slightly reduced coverage at the low frequency end of the tuning range — a high value gives slightly extended coverage in this direction. For short wave applications an air-spaced variable capacitor is generally preferable to an inexpensive solid dielectric type. For a simple receiver of this type a solid dielectric type should be perfectly suitable though.

Wiring up the receiver should not be difficult provided you generously tin with solder all the tags and the ends of the leadout wires prior to making the connections. If you are new to electronics construction it would be as well to practice soldering a few bits of wire together, or something of this type, before trying to build the set. Semiconductor devices are more vulnerable to damage from heat when they are being soldered into circuit than are most other components. The only semiconductor device in this circuit is D1, and as a germanium component this is more vulnerable to heat damage than most semiconductor components (which are mostly constructed from silicon these days). It should not be necessary to use a heatshunt on the leadouts of this component when soldering them into place, but the soldered joints must be completed reasonably quickly. Probably the easiest way of fitting R1 and C2 is to first solder C2 onto R1's leadout wires, then wire this two component assembly in place on SK4.

In Use

The subject of aerials and an earth connection were discussed in the previous chapter, and obviously a simple set of this type benefits greatly from a good aerial and an earth connection for reception on the lower frequency bands. However, even something like an improvised indoor aerial about six or seven metres long should provide a few interesting stations. However, they will mostly be at quite low volume levels.

You should find the broadcast bands easily enough, since these are usually the only source of really strong radio signals. You might occasionally pick up stations in the gaps between the broadcast bands, but these will mostly just be heard as odd noises, and will not be ordinary a.m. transmissions. These stations are mostly such things as direction finding beacons and radio teletype signals, neither of which are of much interest to the short wave listener. The receiver covers a wide range of frequencies, but tuning is still quite easy. The bandwidth of the set is so broad that there is no need for a slow-motion drive.

Normally the aerial is connected to SK1, but if there is a problem in separating two closely spaced stations that are at good volume, try using SK2. This will give reduced signal strengths, but the selectivity should improve a little, possibly enabling one or other of the stations to be tuned in. An earth connection will probably improve reception significantly on the lower frequency bands covered by the receiver, and it is well worth using one if at all possible.

The main requirement when using the receiver is patience. Stations will sometimes come through loud and clear, only to fade out completely after a while. If you wait on the frequency for a while the station will probably return again, and if you monitor the frequency long enough you will probably get the station identification message in the end. This fading is not due to any fault in the receiver. It is simply due to the vagaries of the atmosphere, and while a simple crystal set is ill equipped to deal with the problem, even with a highly sophisticated receiver exactly the same problem can be experienced. The receiver should be capable of picking up a number of European stations over a period of time, including the

English services of some stations, and it might occasionally bring in stations from further afield.

Chapter 3

T.R.F. RECEIVERS

A t.r.f. (tuned radio frequency) receiver is one step up from a crystal type. Although sets of this type are usually very simple, their performance is well beyond that of a crystal set, and they are capable of receiving many stations at virtually any time. In fact their level of performance is higher than one could reasonably expect from such simple circuits. On the other hand, it would be unrealistic to expect a receiver of this type to perform as well as a sophisticated superheterodyne ("superhet") type costing hundreds of pounds. Good as they are, t.r.f. sets do not rival good superhet designs in terms of sensitivity, selectivity, immunity to breakthrough of very strong signals, or ease of use. They have in their favour low cost, ease of construction, and that they require no complicated alignment once finished. They often require no setting up at all once completed, and are ready for immediate use. It has to be admitted that a t.r.f. receiver is more difficult to use than a superhet type. The regeneration control must be very carefully adjusted, and in most cases frequently readjusted, in order to maintain the receiver at optimum performance. However, if you are prepared to put up with their shortcomings, t.r.f. sets can provide a great deal of fun for a minimal monetary outlay.

T.R.F./Superhet

Ready-made radio sets, from simple medium and long wave broadcast receivers through to complex communications receivers, are virtually all of the superhet variety. A receiver of this type takes the incoming radio signal and converts it to the intermediate frequency. Whatever the frequency of the received signal may happen to be, it is always converted to the fixed intermediate frequency. For many receivers this intermediate frequency is at about 455kHz to 470kHz, but a variety of frequencies are used in modern sets that cover the short wave bands. This conversion process might seem to be an unnecessary complication, but it brings tremendous advantages. High gain is relatively easy to obtain at the intermediate frequency, which is normally much lower than the reception frequency. This makes it reasonably simple to obtain good sensitivity. Good selectivity is also quite easy to obtain, since the tuned circuits can have preset tuning, and there is no difficulty in having several of them. Also, there are crystal, mechanical, and ceramic filters available which have excellent performance figures, giving superb selectivity. These types of filter have fixed operating frequencies, but this is not a problem in a superhet design as they can be included in the intermediate frequency stages of the receiver.

With a t.r.f. receiver the signal processing ahead of the detector is all provided at the reception frequency. This is a very simple and straightforward way of handling things, but it gives relatively poor performance. With the radio frequency signal being processed at a comparatively high frequency, both high gain and good selectivity become more difficult to achieve. High gain is likely to be accompanied by instability unless extreme steps are taken to avoid stray feedback. This usually means comprehensively screening off one stage from the next. Several tuned circuits can be used in order to improve selectivity, but each one would require a gang on the tuning capacitor.

It is possible to produce a t.r.f. set of quite good performance, but such a set would probably cost as much as a superhet type, would be equally complex, require alignment before it was ready to use, and would probably still fail to perform as well as a superhet design. In other words, it would have the drawbacks of a superhet without having its advantages. A t.r.f. set is probably only a worthwhile proposition if it is kept simple but effective. The two designs featured in this chapter are simple three and four transistor designs that provide quite good results at minimal cost.

A t.r.f. set could simply consist of a crystal set having an amplifier added ahead of the detector. Such an arrangement brings definite advantages, but leaves a slight problem. On the plus side, the addition of some r.f. gain certainly improves sensitivity, enabling far weaker signals to be received properly. Some amplification of the audio signal can further improve sensitivity. The amplification makes it possible to reduce the loading on the tuned circuit. This is achieved in two ways, and one of these is by having a high input impedance amplifier that places minimal loading on the tuned circuit. The other is by using a more loose coupling from the aerial to the tuned circuit. In addition to reducing loading effects this results in less signal being coupled from the aerial to the receiver, giving lower signal strengths. However, the gain of the receiver gives good results despite this.

Regeneration

The problem that remains is one of selectivity. By reducing the loading on the tuned circuit its effective Q is boosted, and can be something close to its actual Q value. Practical inductors tend not to have particularly high Q values though, and at the high frequencies involved in short wave reception this results in the tuned circuit having a fairly wide bandwidth. In fact the bandwidth of the tuned circuit could easily be enough to swallow up virtually an entire short wave broadcast band, resulting in the set simultaneously receiving practically all the stations on the band! In practice the increase in selectivity over a crystal set would probably not be very great.

The standard way around this problem is to apply "regeneration" over the r.f. amplifier stage and the tuned circuit. Regeneration merely means feeding some of the output of the amplifier back to the input. The general electronic term for this is "feedback", and this can be of the positive and negative varieties. With negative feedback the signal fed back to the input is of the opposite polarity to the input signal, and tends to cancel it out. This reduces gain, broadens the frequency response, and has the opposite effect to the one we require.

Positive feedback is when the fed-back signal and the input signal are of the same polarity, or are what is termed "in-phase". They therefore add together rather than cancelling each other out. Positive feedback increases the gain of an amplifier by effectively increasing the amplitude of the input signal. The increase in gain is not uniform though, and there is more feedback at frequencies close to the resonant frequency of the tuned circuit than there is at frequencies significantly removed from it. This is simply due to the fact that there is slightly

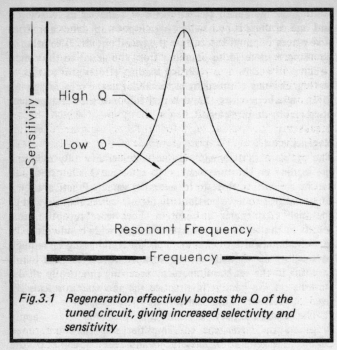

Fig.3.1 Regeneration effectively boosts the Q of the tuned circuit, giving increased selectivity and sensitivity

more gain at frequencies close to the resonant frequency than there is at frequencies a little further away from resonance. As the amount of feedback is increased, the discrepancy in gain at the centre of the passband and slightly removed from it becomes larger. Figure 3.1 shows the effect that positive feedback has on the passband of a receiver.

There is a limit to the amount of feedback that can be usefully applied to the amplifier, as exceeding a certain level results in the circuit breaking into oscillation. In other words, it generates a signal at the resonant frequency of the tuned circuit. This prevents proper reception of ordinary a.m. stations, and would probably result in the receiver transmitting illegal radio interference. However, just below the oscillation point the bandwidth of the receiver will be quite narrow. This gives good reception of a.m. signals with reasonable immunity to adjacent channel interference. A strong signal very close to the one you wish to monitor could still cause problems, but this could happen with even the best of receivers. With the extreme crowding currently found on virtiaully all the short wave bands this is something you just have to learn to live with. It is best regarded as all part of the fun, adding to the challenge of receiving weak DX signals.

It must be stressed that it is very important for the regeneration level to be set just below the point at which the set breaks into oscillation, and for it to be maintained at this level. Even having the regeneration level just slightly short of the optimum setting can substantially degrade the receiver's performance. Unfortunately, even quite small changes in the setting of the tuning control can necessitate slight readjustment of the regeneration control. This is something that tends to be a little inconsistent from one receiver to another, and which is usually better over some parts of the tuning range than others. You can reasonably expect to make frequent readjustments of the regeneration control though. It is this factor that makes a t.r.f. receiver more difficult to use than a superhet type. Fortunately, it is something that you soon get used to, and will do intuitively. It is therefore less of a bind than you might expect.

In the past many regenerative receivers have used a regenerative detector. This utilizes the non-linearity of any currently available amplifying device. With most transistors this manifests itself in the form of an increase in gain as the current through the device increases. This results in one set of half cycles being amplified more than the other set, giving a crude and extremely inefficient form of rectification. Normally the efficiency of a rectifier based on this principle would be so low as to be of no practical value. However, the addition of regeneration greatly exaggerates the difference between the amplification of the two sets of half cycles, giving quite usable results in the present context.

This type of detector was quite popular in receiver designs for the home constructor in the days when semiconductors were very expensive. It is a system which is much less used in current designs. The addition of a diode or two and removal of a resistor or two is not going to make much difference to the overall cost of the receiver. Using a separate detector usually gives slightly better performance, with a lower background noise level. The two receivers featured in this chapter both have ordinary diode detectors. Although they do not have regenerative detectors, they are still regenerative receivers in the sense that they rely on positive feedback to enhance their selectivity. They have regeneration controls that must be accurately adjusted if the receivers are to give good results.

Portable Receiver
This t.r.f. set is a very simple type having preset regeneration and a built-in telescopic aerial. These two factors obviously limit performance, but the set is capable of receiving a number of stations at virtually any time of the day or night. In fact its performance goes well beyond that of a crystal set having a long aerial and an earth connection. Being battery powered and having a built-in aerial, the set is fully portable. Having preset regeneration limits performance to some extent, but it also makes the set very easy to use.

Figure 3.2 shows the full circuit diagram for the portable short wave receiver. Tuning capacitor VC1 and L1 form the tuned circuit, and provide coverage of several short wave broadcast bands. The actual frequency coverage is from around 4.5MHz to 12.5MHz, but this can be moved up or down by decreasing or increasing the value of L1. This type of receiver is not likely to work very well at either extreme of the short wave spectrum though, and I would not recommend any very large changes in L1's value. Because a very short aerial is used it must be coupled direct to the tuned circuit. This limits the selectivity to some extent, but the receiver is generally adequate in this respect.

The r.f. amplifier is a two stage type based on TR1 and TR2. TR1 is a junction gate field effect (Jfet) device which has an extremely high input resistance. Its input impedance is quite low at radio frequencies due to its input capacitance that will typically be around 30p to 50p. However, this capacitance is in parallel with VC1, and in this case becomes part of the tuned circuit. This results in no significant loading on the tuned circuit from the amplifier, and helps to give good performance.

40

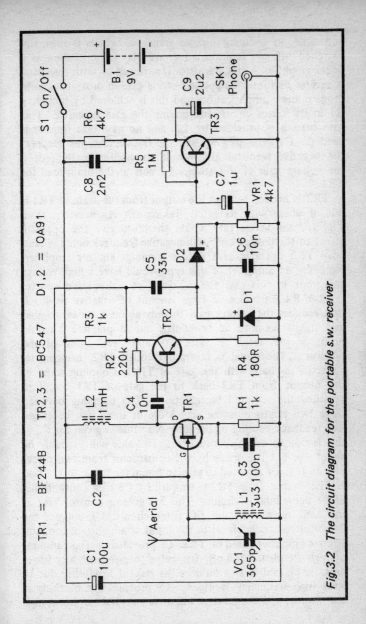

Fig.3.2 The circuit diagram for the portable s.w. receiver

41

Unlike an ordinary bipolar transistor which is normally switched off and requires a forward bias for operation as a linear amplifier, a Jfet transistor is switched on with zero bias. A reverse bias must be applied to the gate in order to accommodate linear amplification, and this is achieved by including R1 in its source circuit and biasing the gate to earth. This gate biasing is provided by L1, and no gate bias resistor is needed. C3 decouples R1 at radio frequencies, and removes the negative feedback that would otherwise greatly reduce the voltage gain of this stage. L2 acts as the drain load for TR1.

TR2 is needed because the output from the drain of TR1 is out of phase with its gate. Taking the regeneration from TR1's drain to its gate would therefore give the opposite effect to the desired one, with negative feedback being obtained. TR2 operates as a simple common emitter amplifier. Normally an amplifier of this type would have a high voltage gain, but in this case the inclusion of unbypassed emitter resistor R4 introduces a large amount of negative feedback that reduces the voltage gain to only about 5 times. Higher gain might seem to be beneficial, but in practice it would probably just result in instability and overloading of the receiver. The signal is inverted through TR2, bringing its collector in-phase with the gate of TR1. Coupling some of the output from TR2 back to the gate of TR1 therefore provides the required regeneration. The coupling between these two points must be very loose or there will be excessive feedback causing oscillation. No value is given for C2 as this is not an ordinary capacitor. Its value will probably be about 1p, but it is made by the constructor from two pieces of wire that are adjusted to give optimum feedback.

The output from TR2 is coupled by C5 to a conventional diode demodulator circuit. This has volume control VR1 as the load resistor in the r.f. filter circuit. C7 couples the demodulated audio signal to the input of a high gain common emitter amplifier based on TR3. C8 provides a certain amount of high frequency roll-off that helps to give a slightly lower noise level, and it also reduces the risk of instability due to stray high frequency feedback. C9 provides d.c. blocking at the output, and the receiver will drive a crystal earphone, high impedance headphones, or medium impedance headphones.

Power is provided by a 9 volt battery, and the current consumption of the circuit is approximately 6 milliamps. A small (PP3) battery will suffice, but if the set is likely to be used a great deal it might be better to use a slightly higher capacity type, such as six HP7 size cells in a plastic holder.

Construction

Stripboard is less than ideal for a project that carries high frequency signals, and problems can arise due to the capacitance between adjacent tracks providing a route for stray coupling. The layout shown in Figure 3.3 (component side) and Figure 3.4 (track side) seems to be free from any problems of this type though. If you are new to electronics construction it would be a good idea to try soldering a few bits of wire to a scrap of stripboard in order to gain some experience before building the circuit board. The soldering iron should be a type having a bit of about 1 to 2.5 millimetres in diameter, and the solder should be a 22 s.w.g. multicored type for use in electrical and electronic work. The heavier gauge (18 s.w.g.) solder is usable, but if this is used it will be necessary to take great care to avoid applying an excessive amount of solder to the joints.

Stripboard is not sold in the required size of 37 holes by 20 copper strips, and a board of this size must therefore be cut down from a larger size using a hacksaw. Cut along rows of holes rather than trying to cut between them. This will leave rather rough cut edges, but they are easily filed flat. Next drill the two mounting holes. Holes of 3.3 millimetres in diameter will suit 6BA or M3 fixings. For plastic stand-offs the diameter of these mounting holes must be chosen to suit the particular type used. Only two cuts in the copper strips are required. There is a special spot face cutter tool that can be used for this task, or a hand-held twist drill of about 5 millimetres in diameter is suitable.

The board is then ready for the components to be fitted. Start with the resistors and capacitors, and then add the semiconductors, leaving D1 and D2 until the end. Note that the electrolytic capacitors must be fitted with the correct polarity. Both the axial (horizontal mounting) and radial (vertical

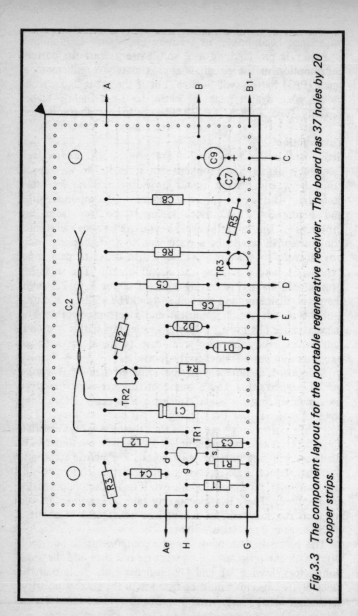

Fig.3.3 The component layout for the portable regenerative receiver. The board has 37 holes by 20 copper strips.

44

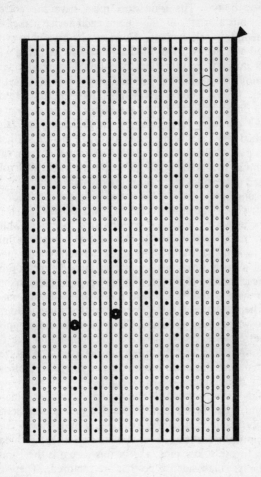

Fig.3.4   The underside of the component panel. Only two breaks in the copper strips are required.

45

mounting) mounting types are normally marked with " + " and (or) " − " signs to show their polarity. Additionally, the axial type invariably have an indentation around the positive end of their body. The transistors must have the correct orientation, but a "flat" on one side of each device makes the correct orientation self evident. However, be careful to avoid any crossed-over wires. The diodes must also be fitted with the correct polarity, and their polarity should be clearly marked by coloured bands around one end of the body (indicating the cathode (" + ") end). Remember that D1 and D2 are germanium diodes, and that they are vulnerable to damage by heat. Take due care to complete each soldered joint fairly quickly when they are being fitted onto the board. A heat-shunt (or a pair of pliers) can be used to extract heat from each leadout wire as it is soldered in place, but provided each joint is completed quite quickly this is not really necessary.

As explained previously, C2 is not an ordinary capacitor. It consists of what is quaintly termed a "twisted pair". This is simply two pieces of insulated wire twisted together. Multi-strand wire is not well suited to this task as it has a definite tendency to untwist itself. The single strand type is much better, and a fairly heavy gauge p.v.c. insulated type is probably the best choice. However, a thinner type or even enamelled copper wire is usable. If you use enamelled wire, make sure that the insulation is not chipped and that there is no risk of the two wires short circuiting. The wires should be about 70 millimetres long, but it may well be found that the full length is not required, and that they can eventually be shortened somewhat. At this stage only twist the wires together over about 10 or 20 millimetres of their length.

The leads from off-board components can be soldered direct to the circuit board, but this is not a very good practice. It can easily result in a copper strip being pulled away from the board, possibly causing short circuits or the strip to break. It is better to use solder pins, and in this case it is the 1 millimetre diameter single-sided type that are required. These are inserted from the underside (copper side) of the board, soldered in place, and then tinned with solder at the top. There should then be no difficulty in soldering a lead to each pin, and even pulling quite hard on a lead is highly unlikely to damage the board in any way.

When the board has been completed it is a good idea to thoroughly check it for errors, immediately correcting any that are located. Also check for any accidental short circuits between adjacent copper strips due to blobs of excess solder or solder splashes. Any excess solder of either type can usually be removed quite easily with the aid of the soldering iron or a sharp modelling knife.

The receiver can be housed in virtually any small plastic or metal case, but it is probably best to choose one that will comfortably accommodate everything so that construction is kept simple and straightforward. The three controls and earphone socket are mounted on the front panel. The exact layout is not too critical but, on the other hand, try to choose one that will avoid long leads and lots of crossed over leads going everywhere. The component panel is mounted on the base panel of the case. If you use ordinary nuts and bolts rather than stand-offs, use some extra nuts or short spacers over the mounting bolts, between the case and the component panel. This avoids having the board buckle and possibly crack as the mounting nuts are tightened.

A hole for the telescopic aerial must be drilled in the top panel of the case, well towards one end of the unit. If the case is a metal type it is essential that the aerial is insulated from it. This can be achieved by using a grommet of appropriate diameter in the mounting hole. Telescopic aerials normally have provision for a fixing screw at the base, and a hole for this must be drilled at the appropriate position in the base panel of the case. The connection to the aerial is made via a soldertag which is fitted over the mounting screw on the inside of the case. The base of the aerial, the soldertag, and the fixing screw must all be insulated from the case if the latter is a metal type. This can be achieved by making the mounting hole in the base panel of the case slightly too large, and using a couple of insulating washers. Figure 3.5 shows the general scheme of things. Some form of continuity tester should be used to help manoeuvre everything accurately into place so that the fixed screw is not in contact with the case. A simple alternative to all this, and the one method I would definitely recommend, is to use a plastic case so that

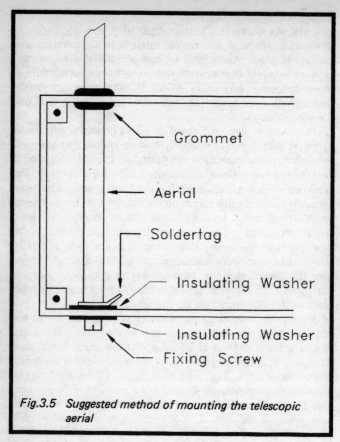

Fig.3.5 *Suggested method of mounting the telescopic aerial*

the problem does not arise in the first place.

The wiring is very straightforward, and the necessary interconnections are shown in Figure 3.6, which should be used in conjunction with Figure 3.3. Point "A" in Figure 3.3 connects to point "A" in Figure 3.6, point "B" connects to point "B", and so on. Ordinary p.v.c. insulated multi-strand connecting wire is used for all this point to point wiring. Keep all the wiring as short and direct as reasonably possible, especially the leads to VC1. These leads must be quite short or the high frequency coverage of the receiver could be

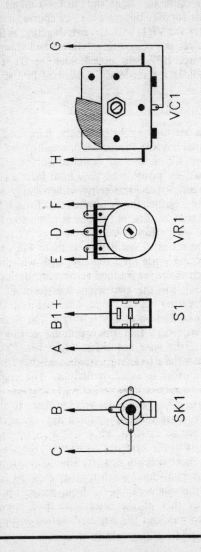

Fig.3.6 Details of the point to point wiring (use in conjunction with Fig.3.3)

seriously reduced. It could also encourage problems with instability and hand-capacity effects (putting your hand near to the tuning control causing a slight shift in the tuning). I used a separate switch for S1, but you can, of course, use a switched potentiometer for VR1, with the switch acting as S1. This control will then act as a conventional on/off and volume control. If you use six HP7 cells in a holder for B1, the connections to the holder are made via a standard PP3 style battery connector.

In Use

Most telescopic aerials are only about one metre long, and in order to give good signal levels the aerial will normally need to be used fully extended. With the set switched on and VR1 well advanced it should be possible to tune in at least a few stations at good strength, but the selectivity will probably not be very good. Twisting together the two wires that form C2 a bit further should improve results, but if this is taken too far the set will break into oscillation at some settings of VC1. It will be clear when the set is in oscillation as there will be a change in the background noise level together with whistling sounds of varying pitch as the set is tuned across a.m. stations.

The optimum setting for the two wires that form C2 is with them twisted together as far as possible without the receiver breaking into oscillation at any setting of the tuning control. You may well find that this optimum setting is achieved with much of the wire not twisted together. You may even find that they have to be untwisted somewhat from their original setting in order to avoid oscillation. The length of the wires can then be reduced somewhat. Whether or not they are left full length, it is a good idea to glue them to the board using an epoxy resin adhesive, making any necessary fine adjustments once the adhesive has set.

Once the adjustment to C2 has been completed, the set is ready for use. Under most conditions there should be plenty of broadcast stations to be found when tuning across its full tuning range. While the selectivity is far from perfect, it is very much better than that of the crystal set, and it will normally be possible to pick out the required station without receiving two or three others at the same time.

Bandspread

Due to its lack of really good selectivity, it is not too difficult to tune in stations using the set, despite its very wide frequency coverage. However, tuning can be made easier using some form of bandspread. This can be of the electrical or mechanical varieties. The mechanical type merely involves fitting a slow-motion drive to the tuning capacitor. Various types are available, mostly offering a reduction ratio of something like 6 to 1 or 8 to 1. There are some relatively expensive types offering a dual reduction ratio of 6 to 1 and 36 to 1. The lower ratio enables the receiver to be tuned fairly rapidly from one end of the tuning range to the other, while the 36 to 1 ratio makes it easy to tune in the receiver very accurately. These slow-motion drives are sometimes in the form of simple shaft and gearing assemblies, but they often include a dial and pointer as well. This type of bandspread is very good, but can considerably complicate the mechanical side of construction. Also, many of these slow-motion drives are quite expensive. Some of them have quite large dials, making them less than ideal for a unit of this type which is designed to be quite small and portable.

For a simple receiver of this type electrical bandspread is probably the more practical arrangement. This merely consists of having a low value variable capacitor connected in parallel with the tuning capacitor, as in Figure 3.7. The low value variable capacitor only provides coverage of a small section of the overall tuning range, but this makes accurate tuning very much easier using this control. The idea is that the main tuning control is used to tune the receiver to the middle of the desired broadcast band, with the receiver then being tuned over that band using the bandspread control. Incidentally, when a set was fitted with a main tuning control and a bandspread type, the tuning control used to be termed the "bandset" control. This term seems to have largely fallen from use these days though.

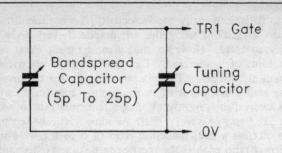

*Fig.3.7 Electrical bandspread merely consists of a low
value variable capacitor in parallel with the tuning
capacitor*

Components for Figure 3.2

Resistors (all 0.25 watt 5% carbon film)
R1   1k (brown, black, red, gold)
R2   220k (red, red, yellow, gold)
R3   1k (brown, black, red, gold)
R4   180R (brown, grey, brown, gold)
R5   1M (brown, black, green, gold)
R6   4k7 (yellow, violet, red, gold)

Potentiometer
VR1   4k7 log

Capacitors
C1   100μ 10V axial elect
C2   see text
C3   100n polyester
C4   10n polyester
C5   33n polyester
C6   10n polyester
C7   1μ 63V radial elect
C8   2n2 mylar or polyester
C9   2μ2 63V radial elect
VC1   365p air spaced variable (Jackson type O)

Semiconductors

TR1	BF244B
TR2	BC547
TR3	BC547
D1	OA91
D2	OA91

Miscellaneous

B1	9 volt (PP3 size)
S1	s.p.s.t. sub-min toggle
SK1	3.5mm jack socket
L1	$3\mu3$ r.f. choke
L2	1m r.f. choke
	Telescopic aerial
	Crystal earphone, medium or high impedance headphones with 3.5mm jack plug
	Battery connector
	Case
	0.1 inch pitch stripboard, 37 holes by 20 copper strips
	Two control knobs
	Wire, solder, fixings, etc.

(A BF244, BF244A, or a 2N3819 are also suitable for TR1, but might require some adjustment to the value of R1 in order to optimise performance.)

T.R.F. Receiver

This second t.r.f. receiver is very firmly based on the design described previously, but it has a few improvements. Firstly, it is designed for use with a long wire aerial, and accordingly it has aerial and earth sockets, with no built-in aerial of any kind. Next, it has a regeneration control so that it can be set for optimum results at any frequency within its tuning range. Finally, it has a buffer stage at the output so that it can be used with lower impedance headphones in addition to those types that are usable with the portable t.r.f. receiver.

The full circuit diagram for the second version of the t.r.f. receiver appears in Figure 3.8. Simply connecting a long aerial direct to the tuned circuit is not acceptable as it would

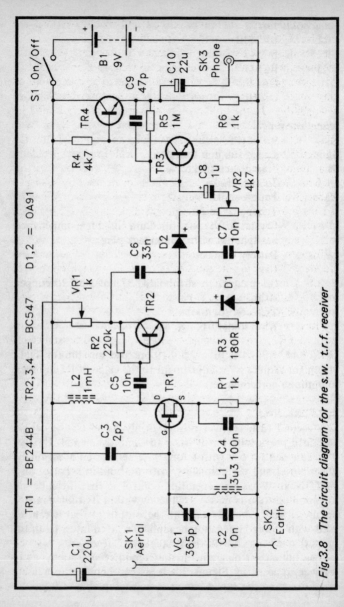

TR1 = BF244B   TR2,3,4 = BC547   D1,2 = 0A91

Fig.3.8 The circuit diagram for the s.w. t.r.f. receiver

excessively damp the tuned circuit and would overload the receiver. The signal could be applied to a tapping on L1, but the set has been deliberately designed to use a simple inductor in the tuned circuit. The plug-in coils that were once available for receivers of this type would not seem to be manufactured any more. Using a simple inductor overcomes problems of availability. In the unlikely event of a suitable choke for L1 being unavailable, it is not a difficult task to wind your own. The lack of any additional windings or tappings on the inductor brings with it a few design problems, but problems that are not too difficult to solve.

The aerial coupling problem is overcome by using a capacitive tapping on the tuned circuit instead of a tapping on L1 (or a low impedance coupling winding on L1). C2 has been placed in series with tuning capacitor VC1, but the high value of C2 ensures that the effective capacitance swing of VC1 is sufficient to give coverage of several bands. The aerial is connected to the junction of VC1 and C2, which effectively forms a tapping near the earth end of the tuned circuit. This method is something less than perfect, but in practice it gives perfectly acceptable results.

Regeneration is applied from the collector of TR2 to the gate of TR1, as in the original design. The load resistance for TR2 is now the track of a potentiometer, with the feedback being taken from its wiper to the gate of TR1 via d.c. blocking capacitor C3. With the wiper of VR1 at the bottom (TR2 collector) end of the track there is full feedback. As the wiper is moved up the track, the signal level reduces, as does the amount of regeneration. With the wiper at the top end of the track there is zero feedback. Therefore, VR1 enables the negative feedback level to be set anywhere from zero to a maximum level that will cause oscillation at any setting of the tuning control.

An important factor with regenerative receivers is the accuracy with which the regeneration can be set near the point at which oscillation occurs. The easiest way of setting the correct regeneration level is often to first advance the regeneration control so that the set just breaks into oscillation, and to then back it off slightly from that point so that oscillation ceases.

Even if you try to carefully advance the regeneration control to just below the oscillation point, you will often end up misjudging it, with the set breaking into oscillation. A common problem is that of the set breaking into oscillation, and then being reluctant to stop! The regeneration control sometimes has to be backed off by a substantial amount in order to halt oscillation, and it may well have to be backed off so far that the set is operating at far from optimum performance once oscillation ceases. This makes accurate adjustment of the regeneration control very difficult indeed. Presumably this effect is due to shifts in the d.c. operating levels of the circuit as it breaks into and eventually drops out of oscillation.

Fortunately, this design seems to be largely free from this problem, and accurate adjustment of the regeneration control is reasonably easy. The precision with which the regeneration control has to be adjusted means that it is always something that has to be carried out very carefully though.

The audio stages consist of a common emitter amplifier that is essentially the same as the one in the original circuit, plus an emitter follower output stage. The latter gives a lower output impedance so that the headphones or earphone do not reduce the output level significantly due to loading effects. In this case the high frequency roll-off is provided by C9 which provides high frequency negative feedback over both audio stages.

Power is supplied by a 9 volt battery, and as the current consumption is likely to exceed 10 milliamps it is advisable to use a reasonably high capacity battery. Six HP7 cells in a plastic holder are a good choice, and will give many hours of operation.

Construction

Like the portable t.r.f. receiver, this one is based on a strip-board that has 37 holes by 20 copper strips. Construction of the board is much the same as the board for the portable receiver, and it will therefore not be described in detail. Figure 3.9 (component side) and Figure 3.10 (underside) show full details of the component layout etc. Although two of the cuts in the copper strips may seem to provide no useful

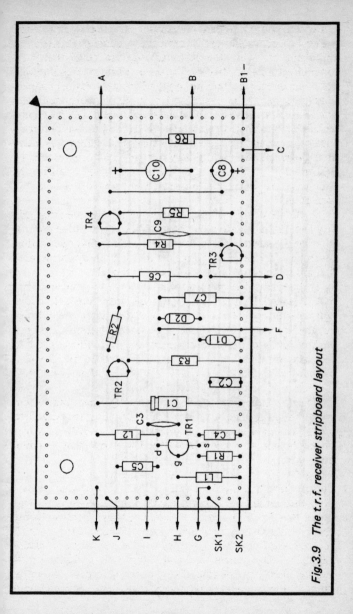

Fig.3.9 The t.r.f. receiver stripboard layout

57

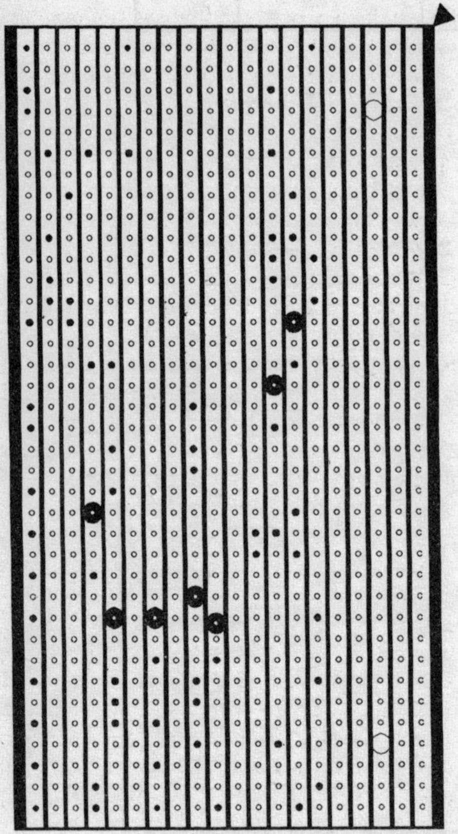

Fig.3.10 The underside of the stripboard panel

function, they are in fact needed to reduce stray coupling due to the small capacitance between the copper strips. If this is not done it is likely that problems with instability (in the form of low frequency oscillation on the output signal) will occur at certain settings of the regeneration control. It is still possible that this could happen, but only if the regeneration control is advanced well beyond the oscillation threshold.

Traditionally, simple short wave receivers are built using an aluminium chassis plus an aluminium front panel, often with no outer casing. The lack of casing was an advantage as these sets usually had band changing via plug-in coils. The absence of an outer casing meant that there was easy access to the coil holder, with no need for any opening flaps in the case to be arranged. This receiver is not primarily intended as a multi-band type having band changing, but with only a single winding and two connections to contend with, it would not be difficult to improvise simple plug-in band changing. It would just be a matter of having some form of two way socket fitted to the board in place of L1, plus some matching plugs fitted with r.f. chokes of various values.

It is worth noting that home constructed coils for a receiver of this type are easily produced. Using a coil former of about 6 millimetres in diameter fitted with a dust iron core, about 18 turns of 24 s.w.g. enamelled copper wire should give coverage of the main short wave broadcast bands. Adjusting the core enables the coverage of the receiver to be shifted upwards or downwards slightly if necessary. A home-made coil of this type is likely to work at least as well as a ready-made r.f. choke, and could well have a higher Q value, giving slightly improved results. Trying higher or lower numbers of turns enables larger shifts in the coverage to be achieved. About 40 turns of wire for instance, should provide coverage of the low frequency bands. It can be very interesting to play about with various coils to see what can be picked up.

Assuming that the set is built as a single band type, a plastic or metal box measuring about 150 by 80 by 50 millimetres or more should accommodate everything. As tuning capacitor VC1 does not have either set of plates connected to earth, my preference would be for a plastic type. This avoids having to insulate VC1 from a metal case, which might not be very

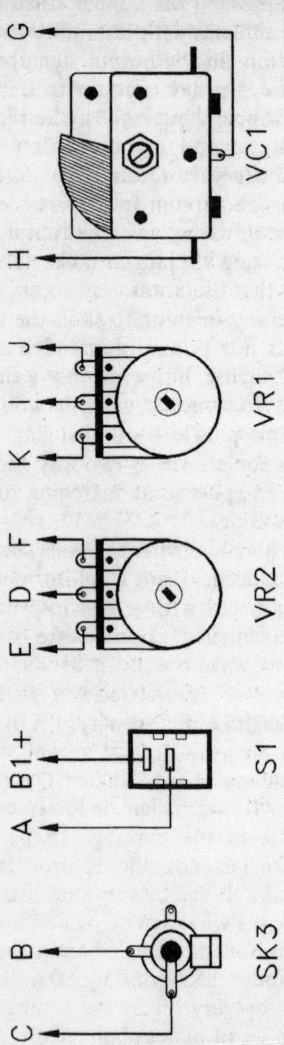

Fig.3.11 Details of the t.r.f. receiver wiring

easily accomplished. The controls and headphone socket are mounted on the front panel, but it will probably be more convenient to have the aerial and earth sockets fitted on the rear panel. Choose a layout that will enable the point to point wiring to be kept reasonably short. Details of this wiring are shown in Figure 3.11, which should be used in conjunction with Figure 3.9.

The selectivity of this receiver is quite good, and the use of some form of bandspread is strongly recommended. Tuning will be quite difficult without the aid of electrical or mechanical bandspread, but the set will just about be usable if VC1 is merely fitted with a large control knob.

In Use

This set is not designed for use with a short aerial, and at the very least an indoor aerial about eight metres long should be connected to SK1. An earth connection is not essential, but should be used where possible. The receiver is used much like any other set, but there is obviously the slight complication of the regeneration control to contend with. With this only moderately advanced you should be able to locate the broadcast bands and receive a few of the stronger transmissions. Select a band, and then advance VR1 as far as possible without the set breaking into oscillation. It should then be possible to tune a number of stations on that band at good strength, but it might be necessary to make some readjustments to VR1 in order to keep the regeneration at the optimum level. With luck, you will find that setting the regeneration control with the set tuned to the middle of a band will give good reception over the entire band, with no further adjustment of VR1 being necessary.

Components for Figure 3.8

Resistors (all 0.25 watt 5% carbon film)
R1	1k (brown, black, red, gold)
R2	220k (red, red, yellow, gold)
R3	180R (brown, grey, brown, gold)
R4	4k7 (yellow, violet, red, gold)
R5	1M (brown, black, green gold)
R6	1k (brown, black, red, gold)

Potentiometers
VR1	1k lin
VR2	4k7 log

Capacitors
C1	220μ 10V axial elect
C2	10n polyester
C3	2p2 ceramic plate
C4	100n polyester
C5	10n polyester
C6	33n polyester
C7	10n polyester
C8	1μ 63V radial elect
C9	47p ceramic plate
C10	22μ 16V radial elect
VC1	365p air spaced (Jackson type O)

Semiconductors
TR1	BF244B
TR2	BC547
TR3	BC547
TR4	BC547
D1	OA91
D2	OA91

Miscellaneous
L1	3μ3 r.f. choke
L2	1m r.f. choke
SK1	Red 4mm socket
SK2	Black 4mm socket

SK3	3.5mm jack socket
B1	9 volt (6 x HP7 in holder)
S1	s.p.s.t. sub-min toggle
	Case
	0.1 inch pitch stripboard, 37 holes by 20 strips
	Crystal earphone, high impedance headphones, or medium impedance headphones, with 3.5mm jack plug
	Battery connector
	Three control knobs
	Wire, solder, fixings, etc.

Chapter 4

AMATEUR BANDS RECEIVER

Ordinary amplitude modulation was once used a great deal on the short wave amateur bands, but currently it is something you may never encounter on these bands. If we exclude methods of communication that involve computers, teletype machines, or something of this nature (all of which go well beyond the scope of this book), the only two methods of modulation that are used to any extent on the short wave amateur bands are c.w. (continuous wave – or morse code) and single sideband (s.s.b.). The latter is a form of voice communication. Signals of both these types can be received using a simple t.r.f. receiver, if it has the regeneration adjusted marginally beyond the threshold of oscillation. Although this provides only a very crude method of demodulation, it can actually be quite effective. It is less than ideal though, and runs the risk of the receiver radiating illegal interference.

For reception on the amateur bands using a simple receiver there is a definite advantage in having a receiver that is specifically designed for the job, rather than doing the best you can with a t.r.f. set. The receiver described in this chapter is specifically designed for amateur bands reception, and is totally unsuitable for use on the broadcast bands. It can not resolve ordinary a.m. signals properly, but works well with both c.w. and s.s.b. types. It is of the "direct conversion" type, and these receivers are also known as "homodyne" sets.

S.S.B.
It is by no means essential to have an understanding of s.s.b. transmissions in order to tune them in. On the other hand, it is a definite advantage. You may prefer to skip over this explanation of s.s.b., but I would strongly recommend that you should at least quickly read through it once. While s.s.b. is an extremely effective method of voice communication, it also presents some practical difficulties.

Tuning in an s.s.b. transmission is not as straightforward as tuning in an a.m. station. With an a.m. signal a slight lack of accuracy in the tuning is unlikely to have any great effect on results. Pick up of the signal will be something less than optimum, and any adjacent channel interference will be increased slightly, but the transmission will probably be perfectly readable. On a strong station even quite large tuning errors of about 2kHz or even more can produce a perfectly intelligible output. The situation is very different with s.s.b. signals where even a tuning error of one or two hundred hertz can render the audio output difficult or impossible to understand.

The pitch of the audio output signal during s.s.b. reception is dependent on the tuning being spot-on. Any lack of tuning accuracy is reflected in an error in the pitch of audio signal. A tuning error in one direction results in the audio pitch being too high by an amount equal to the tuning error. An error of (say) 200Hz, therefore gives an audio output that has every frequency shifted upwards by 200Hz. This gives what is called, for obvious reasons, the "Donald Duck" effect! Having all the frequencies raised by a small amount does not greatly affect intelligibility, but it does produce rather unnatural sounding results. A large tuning error in this direction will certainly hinder intelligibility, and could make it impossible to understand more than the odd word here and there.

A small tuning error in the opposite direction results in all the audio output frequencies being shifted downwards by an amount equal to the tuning error. This seems to have more serious consequences for the intelligibility than does an equal tuning error in the opposite direction. A larger tuning error in this direction produces a complete scrambling of the signals. The audio output is still recognisable as a human voice, but it is not possible to understand a single word! What actually happens in an extreme case is a form of signal inversion, with the high frequencies being changed to low frequencies, and low frequencies being changed to high frequencies. This is actually the method of voice scrambling used in many security scrambling systems.

The importance of accurate tuning, and maintaining accurate tuning, should now be apparent. With the type of s.s.b. used on the amateur bands there is no certain way of knowing the correct setting for the tuning control, and the tuning has to be done "by ear". In practice the tuning can be set quite accurately in this way, and with a little experience you can usually set the tuning within about 50Hz of the right frequency. Being practical about it, provided the output sounds natural and easy to understand, any slight tuning error is of no real importance.

An s.s.b. signal could be regarded as an ordinary a.m. type with certain parts of the signal missing. In fact an s.s.b. signal can be generated by first producing an ordinary a.m. signal and then filtering out the parts of the signal that are not wanted. This is basically the system used in a "filter" type s.s.b. generator. There are other methods, but these all really boil down to using some form of complex signal phasing in order to cause the unwanted parts of the signal to be cancelled out.

An s.s.b. signal is most easily understood if we first consider the constituent parts of an ordinary a.m. signal. Here we are considering the signal in terms of the frequencies present, and the relative strengths of these constituent signals. Figure 4.1 helps to explain the basic make up of an a.m. signal, and as can be seen from this, the carrier wave is at the middle of things. With no audio input to the transmitter the carrier wave is the only signal present at the output. If an audio signal is used to modulate the carrier wave, this results in sidebands being generated above and below the carrier wave. These are called the upper sideband and lower sideband respectively.

In our simple example of Figure 4.1 there are three audio input frequencies of 500Hz, 1.5kHz, and 2.5kHz. This results in upper sideband components 500Hz, 1.5kHz, and 2.5kHz above the carrier wave. The relative strengths of the sideband components are the same as the relative strengths of the audio input signals that produced them. The lower sideband has components 500Hz, 1.5kHz, and 2.5kHz below the carrier wave, and they are at the same amplitudes as the equivalent signals in the upper sideband.

Suppressed Carrier
The carrier wave is not an essential part of the signal, as it is a simple single frequency signal that carries no vital information. In an s.s.b. signal it is suppressed, usually by using a special

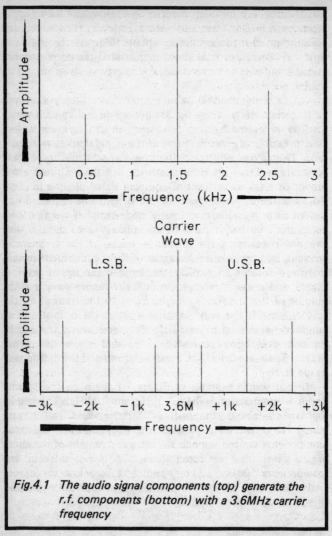

Fig.4.1 The audio signal components (top) generate the r.f. components (bottom) with a 3.6MHz carrier frequency

balanced modulator that phases it out. In a filter type s.s.b. generator a balanced modulator is normally used, with the filtering providing further attenuation of the carrier wave.

Strictly speaking, in order to perfectly demodulate the signal it is necessary to have the carrier signal, since perfectly demodulation requires the frequency and phase information contained in it. However, for voice communications a simple oscillator at the receiver can provide a signal that effectively replaces the carrier wave, and any frequency or phasing errors will not prevent a good quality audio output from being obtained.

It is only fair to point out that this slightly "hit and miss" method of demodulation is not adequate for the transmission and reception of music. Since amateur radio s.s.b. transmissions are only voice types, this is of no consequence in the current context. There is currently a plan for short wave broadcast stations to use s.s.b. instead of ordinary a.m., but this would require a more sophisticated system of s.s.b. transmission and reception in order to permit music signals to be handled properly. The system likely to be used is one where the carrier wave is reduced rather than suppressed, enabling it to be boosted back to full strength at the receiver. For those interested in DXing rather than music reception, a simple receiver of this type should be perfectly adequate for reduced carrier wave s.s.b. reception.

The upper and lower sideband signals contain exactly the same information, and removing one or the other of them still leaves a signal from which the original audio signal can be easily extracted. In a single sideband signal one of the sidebands is suppressed. The signal is either an upper sideband or a lower sideband type, depending on which sideband is left. There is an obvious advantage in removing the carrier wave in that it enables all the transmitter's output power to be concentrated in the part of the signal that really counts — the sidebands. Simply removing one sideband and doubling the power of the other does not actually result in any increase in the total sideband power, and on the face of it gives no advantage.

There are actually a couple of advantages, and one of these is that a single sideband signal occupies slightly under half the space of a double sideband type. With the current crowding on many of the short wave bands this is a tremendous advantage, since it permits more than twice as many stations to be fitted into each band. The second advantage is that it permits the receiver bandwidth to be reduced with no ill effects on the audio output being evident. The reduced receiver bandwidth helps to give a lower background noise level. It is only fair to point out that this is only a real advantage if the receiver is a sophisticated type having filters that produce suitably sharp selectivity. A simple receiver of the type described here is not really able to take advantage of the smaller bandwidth of s.s.b. signals.

Direct Conversion

An ordinary diode demodulator, as used in the crystal set and t.r.f. receivers, is not able to handle s.s.b. signals properly, as it relies upon the input signal including the carrier wave. The audio output produced by an s.s.b. signal using an ordinary diode demodulator sounds a bit like a human voice, but is so distorted as to be totally unintelligible. It is possible to feed the output of an oscillator into the input of a diode demodulator, together with the s.s.b. signal, in order to obtain a crude form of demodulation. This is effectively what is being done when a t.r.f. receiver is used to demodulate an s.s.b. signal by adjusting the regeneration level beyond the oscillation threshold. Some short wave superhet receivers use what is basically just an ordinary a.m. demodulator plus an oscillator (the "b.f.o.", or "beat frequency oscillator") for c.w. and s.s.b. reception. This method works, but it gives less than optimum results.

For really good s.s.b. reception it is necessary to use a special type of demodulator called a "product detector". The basic action of a product detector is to mix two signals, but not in a simple summing fashion, as in an audio mixer, where the output voltage is simply equal to the sum of the two input voltages. With a product detector the gain from one input to the output is controlled by the voltage at the other input. The gain from one input to the output rises and falls in sympathy with the voltage at the other input. With two a.c. input signals, one signal modulates the other signal, giving a complex mixing action. The point of this type of mixing is that it generates sum and difference signals. Here we are talking in terms of input frequencies, and not input voltages. This form of mixing is termed "heterodyning" incidentally.

As a simple example, assume that there are input frequencies at 3.5MHz and 3.6MHz. The sum signal is at 7.1MHz (3.5MHz + 3.6MHz = 7.1MHz) and the difference signal is at 100kHz (3.6MHz − 3.5MHz = 0.1MHz or 100kHz). The two input signals may appear at the output, or one or both of them might be suppressed by a phase cancelling technique. With a non-balanced mixer both input signals appear at the output. With a single balanced type one input signal appears at the output, and with a double balanced mixer both input signals are suppressed.

If we apply a product detector to s.s.b. demodulation, the s.s.b. signal is applied to one input and the output from an oscillator operating at the same frequency as the suppressed carrier wave is applied to the other input. If we go back to our example of Figure 4.1, and take the upper sideband, this has frequencies 500Hz, 1.5kHz, and 2.5kHz above the 3.6MHz carrier wave frequency. In the product detector this gives difference frequencies at 500Hz, 1.5kHz, and 2.5kHz. Taking the 1.5kHz signal as an example, this gives an upper sideband component at 3600001.5kHz, producing a difference frequency of 1.5kHz (3600001.5kHz − 3600000kHz = 1.5kHz). In other words, the difference frequency produces the required audio output frequencies. Obviously there is also the sum frequency at the output, and possibly one or both the input frequencies as well. These do not pose any great problem though, since they are at frequencies well removed from the wanted audio signals. Simple lowpass filtering is sufficient to remove them.

If we now consider the lower sideband signal, the difference frequency again provides the required audio output signal. If you take any of the lower sideband frequencies and deduct them from the 3.6MHz (360000kHz) carrier wave, the answer will always be the appropriate audio frequency. By using the correct oscillator frequency, both lower sideband (l.s.b.) and upper sideband (u.s.b.) signals can be resolved. With a simple receiver of the type described here, there is no need to have any u.s.b./l.s.b. switching. The receiver is equally responsive to signals on each side of the oscillator frequency. This is something of a drawback, since if you tune to (say) a lower sideband signal, the receiver is open to adjacent channel interference from any signal just above the oscillator frequency. In high quality short wave receivers, filters are used to attenuate signals on the wrong side of the oscillator frequency. These receivers consequently require l.s.b./u.s.b. switching. With a direct conversion receiver it is not possible to include filtering of this type, and a slightly wider than optimum bandwidth is something that has to be accepted. Even with today's often crowded band conditions a simple direct conversion receiver will usually still provide excellent results.

A product detector is perfectly suitable for c.w. reception. A c.w. signal consists of just the carrier wave, which is switched on when the morse key is depressed, and off when it is released. The term "continuous wave" seems to be singularly inappropriate for this type of signal, which is clearly far from continuous. I think I am correct in stating that the term is derived from the fact that when present, the carrier wave is continuous in that it is free from any form of modulation, and is a straightforward signal at the operating frequency of the transmitter. In order to demodulate a c.w. signal it is merely necessary to place the oscillator frequency just above or just below the transmission frequency. This gives an audio output frequency from the product detector during the periods when the c.w. signal is keyed on. By varying the frequency offset between the transmission and the oscillator you can obtain any audio output frequency you like (within reason). In practice it is just a matter of tuning the receiver for whatever audio tone you like best, and unlike tuning in an s.s.b. signal, the tuning is not very critical. Whether the tone is a few hundred hertz or a few kilohertz, the signal should be equally easy to copy.

Figure 4.2 shows the stages used in this simple direct conversion receiver. A tuned circuit at the input severely attenuates out of band signals, and helps to avoid overloading of the input stages of the receiver. The bandwidth of this filter is quite wide, and does not significantly aid the selectivity of the receiver. With a direct conversion receiver the selectivity is not determined by the r.f. filtering at all, but is achieved by audio filtering on the output side of the receiver. It is this lack of dependence on r.f. filtering that enables a set of this type to

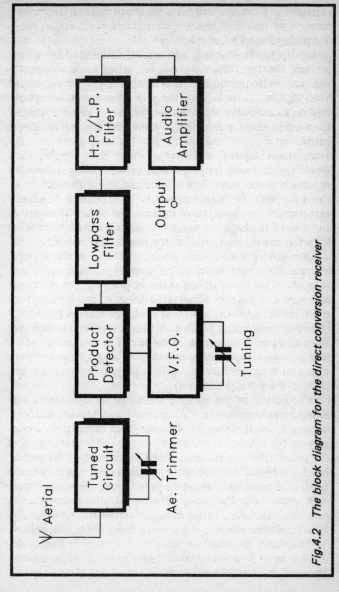

Fig.4.2   The block diagram for the direct conversion receiver

perform well on the crowded amateur bands, and it is this factor that makes it much more suitable for amateur bands reception than a t.r.f. receiver.

Some r.f. amplification and further filtering ahead of the product detector would be helpful, giving improved sensitivity and better immunity to breakthrough of strong out of band signals. However, for the sake of low cost and simplicity no r.f. amplifier stage is used in this receiver, but it seems to provide quite good results none the less. With direct conversion receivers most of the gain has to be provided in the audio stages anyway, and large amounts of r.f. amplification would simply result in the product detector being overloaded for much of the time. The other input of the product detector is fed with the output signal of a v.f.o. (variable frequency oscillator). This oscillator is tuned to the carrier frequency of the desired transmission, and the tuning control of this stage is therefore the tuning control of the receiver as a whole.

On the output side of the product detector there is a simple lowpass filter that removes the sum signal, plus any breakthrough of the input signals at the output. Next there is some highpass and lowpass filtering to improve the selectivity of the receiver. Although shown as a separate stage in Figure 4.2, this filtering is actually of a very simple type, and is built into the audio amplifier section of the circuit. The audio amplifier is a high gain type which provides virtually all the receiver's gain (there is actually a small amount of conversion gain through the product detector).

The output of the receiver is suitable for medium or high impedance headphones. As pointed out previously, headphones or an earphone tend to be much better than a loudspeaker for DXing. It would be possible to feed the output of the receiver to a small audio power amplifier and loudspeaker, but I would not recommend this. Direct conversion receivers tend to be vulnerable to problems with microphony (components, particularly the tuning capacitor in this case, acting like microphones). This design certainly suffers from microphony to a significant degree. When using headphones this unlikely to be of any practical significance, but when using a loudspeaker there is a very real risk of problems due to acoustic feedback, including "howl around".

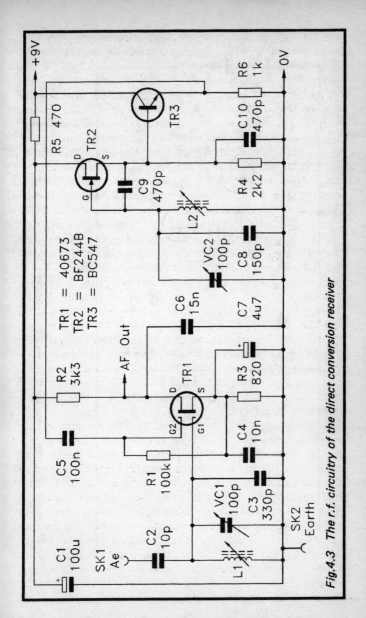

Fig.4.3 The r.f. circuitry of the direct conversion receiver

75

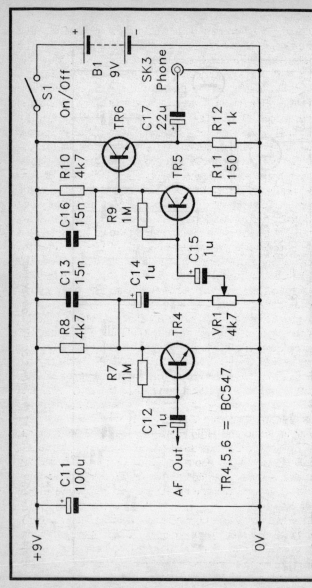

Fig.4.4 The audio circuitry of the direct conversion receiver

The Circuit

The circuit diagram for the r.f., product detector, and oscillator stages of the receiver are shown in Figure 4.3. The circuit for the audio stages is shown separately in Figure 4.4. Starting with the r.f. circuitry, L1, C3, and VC1 form a parallel tuned circuit at the input of the receiver, and these provide the attenuation of out of band signals. VC1 enables received signals to be peaked, and this is what is normally termed an "aerial trimmer" control. The aerial is loosely coupled to the tuned circuit via low value capacitor C2. The specified value should give good results, but with a relatively short aerial a higher value might be better, or connecting the aerial direct to the tuned circuit might give the best results. On the other hand, with a long aerial, or when conditions are producing very strong signals, a lower value might be needed to prevent breakthrough of unwanted signals. It is worth experimenting with different values for C2, or you could opt for several aerial sockets coupled to the tuned circuit via capacitors of different values. The most appropriate socket for the aerial and prevailing band conditions could then be selected.

The product detector is based on dual gate MOSFET TR1. The input signal is applied to gate 1 of this deivce, and L1 biases it to the negative supply rail. The gain from gate 1 to the output is controlled by the gate 2 voltage, and this is given a small positive bias via R1 from the source terminal of TR1. The output of the oscillator is coupled to the gate 2 terminal of TR1, and by varying the gate 2 voltage it provides the required complex mixing and heterodyne effect. As TR1 must handle audio and radio frequency signals, it has both r.f. and a.f. bypass capacitors in its source circuit (C4 and C7 respectively) to ensure good efficiency over both frequency ranges. R2 is the drain load resistor for TR1, and in conjunction with C6 it provides the r.f. filtering at the output of the product detector.

TR2 acts as the basis of a simple and conventional oscillator circuit. TR2 operates in the source follower mode and makes use of a capacitive divider (C9 and C10) to provide a voltage step-up that permits oscillation to be sustained. L2 is the inductive component in the oscillator tuned circuit, and VC2 is the tuning control. As already pointed out, highly accurate tuning is essential if an s.s.b. signal is to be resolved properly, and consequently some form of bandspread is essential if the receiver is to be usable. If VC2 is not fitted with a slow motion drive, a variable capacitor of about 5p or 10p in value should be connected in parallel with VC2 to provide electrical bandspread. TR3 acts as a buffer stage at the output of the oscillator. This ensures that the oscillator is not loaded to the point where it tends to stall. It also helps to avoid problems with pulling of the oscillator. In particular, for practical purposes it avoids problems with the tuning being shifted when adjustments to the aerial trimmer control are made.

Turning now to Figure 4.4, TR4 operates as a high gain common emitter amplifier. Its output is coupled to the volume control (VR1), and from here the signal is coupled to a second high gain common emitter stage (TR5). Due to the inclusion of R11, and the local negative feedback which it provides, this stage operates at something less than full gain. However, running the stage at maximum gain would probably not genuinely aid sensitivity since weak signals would tend to be lost in a high background noise level, rather than being boosted to a more audible level. There would also be an increased risk of instability due to stray feedback. TR6 acts as an emitter follower buffer stage at the output of the unit. C13 and C16, together with the r.f. filter capacitor in the product detector circuit, provide some lowpass filtering that helps to improve the selectivity of the receiver. The values of the coupling capacitors provide a certain amount of highpass filtering that also aids selectivity.

Power is obtained from a 9 volt battery. The current consumption of the set is about 10 milliamps, which is slightly too high to permit economic operation from a small (PP3 size) 9 volt battery. A higher capacity type is more suitable, such as a PP9 (or equivalent) or six HP7 size cells in a plastic battery holder.

Construction

Details of the stripboard panel for the direct conversion receiver are shown in Figure 4.5 (top side) and Figure 4.6 (copper side). This is based on a board having 47 holes by

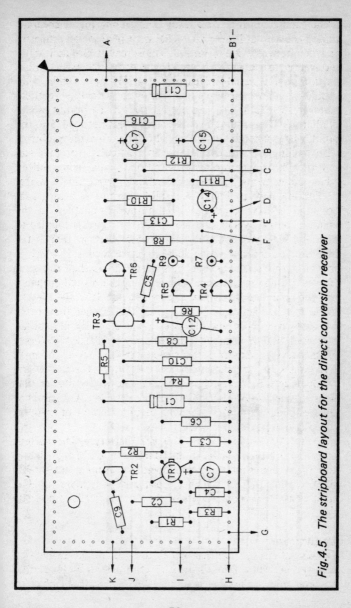

Fig.4.5   The stripboard layout for the direct conversion receiver

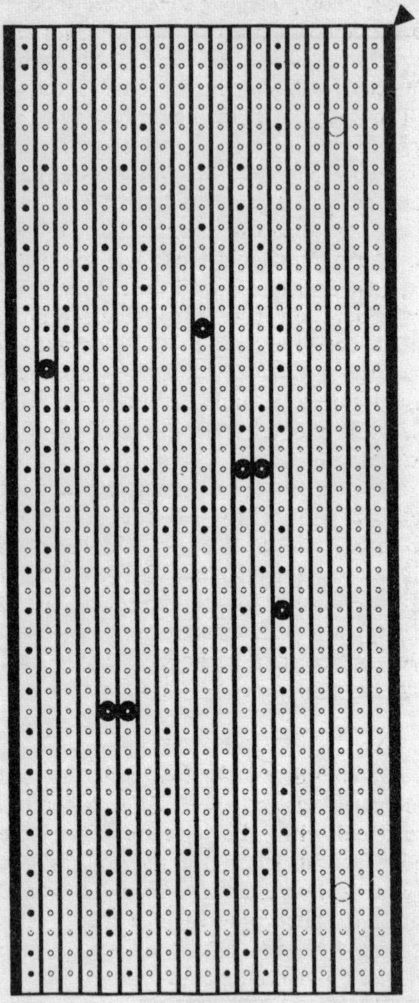

Fig. 4.6 The underside of the component panel

19 copper strips. I will not describe construction of the board in great detail since it follows along much the same lines as construction of the component panels described earlier.

One point worth mentioning is that the dual gate MOSFET used for TR1 is a static sensitive device. It will probably be supplied with a piece of wire shorting all four leadout wires to its metal case. This piece of wire should be left in position until construction of the unit has been completed, but it must, of course, be removed before the unit is tested (although nothing should be damaged if you should forget to remove it before switching on). A 40673 is specified for TR1, but any similar dual gate MOSFET should work well in the circuit. Note that some similar devices do not have the metal shorting clip for static protection, but instead have built-in protection diodes that render special handling precautions unnecessary. A BF244B is specified for the TR2 position, and using this device should ensure consistent and reliable results. However, the unit should work properly using a BF244, BF244A, 2N3819, of any similar Jfet.

There should be no difficulty in fitting the unit into any medium size metal or plastic box. If the unit is to work properly it is essential that the leads to VC1 and VC2 are kept quite short, and to some extent this will dictate the overall layout of the unit. In other respects the general layout of the receiver is not particularly critical. Details of the wiring to the controls and sockets is shown in Figure 4.7, which should be used in conjunction with Figure 4.5.

Coils

So far we have not considered the two coils (L1 and L2). These are home constructed, and are based on 6mm or ¼ inch diameter formers fitted with adjustable dust iron cores. A suggested method of construction for the coils is shown in Figure 4.8. The base section of the coil former has two holes, and a small soldertag is bolted onto each of these. These act as anchor points for the ends of the 24 s.w.g. enamelled copper wire that is used to wind the coils.

The number of turns required depends on the band you wish to receive. I would suggest the 80 metre amateur band as a good starting point. This will usually provide some

81

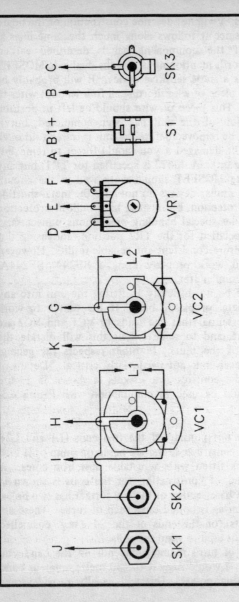

Fig. 4.7 The wiring to the controls and sockets

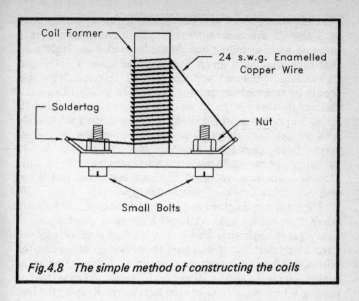

Fig.4.8 The simple method of constructing the coils

stations during daylight hours, with more stations, including some more distant ones, usually being receivable during the hours of darkness. For all bands the two coils are identical, and for the 80 metre band they should have 22 turns of wire. The coils should be wound as tightly as possible, in a single layer, with the smallest possible gap between turns.

About 50 turns on each coil should permit the 160 metre band to be received, but this is mainly used for local contacts, and is now little used in many parts of the country. If you do try the receiver on this band it will be necessary to use a thinner gauge of wire (about 30 s.w.g.), and to have the coil more than one layer of wire deep. The coil does not need to be very neat, but keep all the turns going in the same direction.

Operation on 40 metres is possible using 9 turns of wire on each coil. The set seems to work quite well on this band most of the time, despite the potential breakthrough problem from powerful stations on the nearby 41 metre broadcast band.

The set can be made to operate on the 20 metre amateur band, but the relatively high frequencies involved make it important to have the wiring to VC1 and VC2 very short, as

83

must the wiring to L1 and L2. It also requires modifications to a few of the capacitor values. Each coil should have 7 turns of wire, and the turns should be spaced out slightly so that each winding is about 8 millimetres long. C3, C9, and C10 should be reduced to 100p, 150p, 270p respectively. C8 should be removed altogether. It might be possible to get the receiver to work on the 15 metre, 17 metre, 12 metre, and 10 metre bands, but it would probably not provide a worthwhile level of performance on these bands. Operation on the 30 metre band should be possible, and the receiver would probably operate quite well at the frequencies involved here. However, this is a very small and little used band that is not well suited to a simple receiver of this type.

The coils can be glued in position on the case, but I simply wired them direct onto VC1 and VC2 using short pieces of heavy gauge single-strand wire. This method is admittedly not particularly neat, but it does have the advantage of keeping the wiring to L1 and L2 as short as possible. There is a potential problem with the signal radiated by L2 being picked up by L1, causing a high noise level or even instability. Keeping the two coils well apart helps to minimise the risk, as does placing an aluminium screen between them. A screen simply consists of a small sheet of aluminium that is earthed to the negative supply rail, and fixed between the coils so as to partition them from one another.

Adjustment and Use
Looking on the bright side, the coils do not have to be constructed with great accuracy since the adjustable cores permit their values to be varied over quite wide limits. On the deficit side, this means that adjustment of the cores permits a wide range of frequencies to be covered, and getting them set so that the receiver covers the right band can be difficult. Ideally a frequency meter, a calibrated r.f. signal generator, or a calibrated short wave receiver that covers the appropriate band is required. If a frequency meter is available, measure the output frequency at the emitter of TR3, and adjust the core of L2 so that VC2 provides coverage of a suitable frequency range. Refer to Table 2 in Chapter 1 for a full list of short wave amateur band frequency ranges.

A short wave receiver having a short piece of wire as an aerial can be used to pick up the signal from the receiver's v.f.o., and the tuning scale will then show the v.f.o.'s operating frequency. The short wave set is then effectively acting as a frequency meter, making it relatively straightforward to adjust the core of L2 for the required frequency coverage.

An r.f. signal generator can have its output loosely coupled to the aerial socket, and its output frequency can then be adjusted until its signal is received by the direct conversion receiver. The frequency on the signal generator's tuning dial will then be equal to the receiver's reception frequency. This effectively enables the signal generator to act as a frequency meter, again permitting the core of L2 to be easily set up for the correct frequency coverage.

In order to give the core of L1 the correct setting, first tune in a station using VC2, and adjust VC1 to a setting which matches that of VC2. Then simply adjust the core of L1 for maximum signal strength. Adjustments of VC2 will require readjustment of VC1 in order to maintain optimum sensitivity. This could be avoided by using a twin gang component for VC1 and VC2, but a two gang component of suitable value would probably be unobtainable. Anyway, having separate tuning and aerial trimmer controls avoids any mistracking problems, and ensures that the receiver can be kept operating at optimum sensitivity over its full frequency coverage. It is important to keep the aerial tuned circuit at the correct frequency, not just to give good sensitivity, but also in order to minimise problems with breakthrough of strong out of band signals.

If no means of determining the operating frequency of the receiver is available to you, the only way of finding a suitable setting for the core of L2 is trial and error. This could be rather time consuming though, and may well leave the frequency coverage of the receiver slightly lacking in accuracy. The 160 metre amateur band should not be too difficult to locate, as it lies just slightly on the high frequenty side of the medium wave band. It may be devoid of amateur signals, but there is no harm in winding suitable coils and giving this band a try out to determine how much activity there is on the band in your particular area.

The 80 metre band might be a little more difficult to find. With the core of L2 well screwed in you might find some strong broadcast stations on the 75 metre broadcast band (the BBC World Service and one or two other strong European stations are often to be found on this band). The 80 metre band is just on the low frequency side of this band, and so screwing the core in a little further should bring in reception of this band. It is most easily located in the evenings, especially at weekends, when this band is usually crammed with stations. Apart from making it easier to locate the band, this also makes it easier to guesstimate likely frequency limits for the band.

Finding the 40 metre band is not difficult since it is on the low frequency side of the 41 metre broadcast band. Where one band ends the other starts, with no gap between them. Again, the evenings, especially at weekends, is the time when there is likely to be a good selection of signals that will make the band easy to locate. If you can not find the 40 metre band, you probably tuned to the wrong broadcast band initially. Try adjusting the core of L2 to locate another broadcast band. Remember to keep L1 and VC1 properly peaked when looking for stations.

The 20 metre band is likely to be quite difficult to locate without the aid of any frequency measuring equipment. There is no option but to adjust L2 over its full adjustment range until the band is located, making as many attempts as are needed. Remember that 20 metres tends to fade out at night, and that it is generally well populated in the evenings before darkness falls.

Components for Figures 4.3 and 4.4

Resistors (all 0.25 watt 5% carbon film)
R1   100k (brown, black, yellow, gold)
R2   3k3 (orange, orange, red, gold)
R3   820 (grey, red, brown, gold)
R4   2k2 (red, red, red, gold)
R5   470 (yellow, violet, brown, gold)
R6   1k (brown, black, red, gold)
R7   1M (brown, black, green, gold)

R8	4k7 (yellow, violet, red, gold)
R9	1M (brown, black, green, gold)
R10	4k7 (yellow, violet, red, gold)
R11	150 (brown, green, brown, gold)
R12	1k (brown, black, red, gold)

Potentiometer
VR1	4k7 log

Capacitors
C1	100μ 10V axial elect
C2	10p polystyrene
C3	330p polystyrene
C4	10n polyester
C5	100n polyester
C6	15n polyester
C7	$4\mu7$ 63V radial elect
C8	150p polystyrene
C9	470p polystyrene
C10	470p polystyrene
C11	100μ 10V axial elect
C12	1μ 63V radial elect
C13	15n polyester
C14	1μ 63V radial elect
C15	1μ 63V radial elect
C16	15n polyester
C17	22μ 16V radial elect
VC1	100p air spaced variable (Jackson C804)
VC2	100p air spaced variable (Jackson C804)

Semiconductors
TR1	40673 or similar
TR2	BF244B or similar
TR3	BC547
TR4	BC547
TR5	BC547
TR6	BC547

Miscellaneous
S1	s.p.s.t. miniature toggle

SK1	Red 4mm socket
SK2	Black 4mm socket
SK3	3.5mm jack socket
B1	9 volt (PP9 or six HP7 size cells in holder)
L1	see text
L2	see text
	Case
	0.1 inch matrix stripboard 47 holes by 19 copper strips
	Control knob (3 off)
	¼ inch or 6mm diameter coil formers with adjustable dust iron cores (2 off)
	24 s.w.g. enamelled copper wire
	6BA or M3 soldertags (4 off)
	Wire, solder, fixings, solder pins, etc.

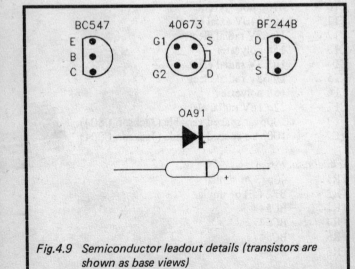

Fig.4.9 Semiconductor leadout details (transistors are shown as base views)